MYSTERIES OF THE UNKNOWN

This book is three adventures into the unknown, all brought together in one volume

G000043140

This book belongs to

_____

_____

_____

ALL ABOUT MONSTERS

This ferocious, fire-breathing dragon is only one of the many imaginary beasts of myths and legends from all over the world.

Enormous lake monsters have been sighted in many parts of the world. Some scientists believe that they may be prehistoric creatures which have somehow survived until the present day.

Ape-men like this and their giant footprints have been reported in the Himalayan mountains and in remote areas of North America.

Credits

All about Monsters was written by
Carey Miller

Art and editorial direction
David Jefferis

Text editing and additional research
Sue Jacquemier
Ingrid Selberg

Design assistant
Iain Ashman

Picture research
Caroline Lucas

Natural history consultant
Dr L B Halstead PhD DSc

Illustrators
John Francis
Malcolm McGregor
Michael Roffe
Christine Howes
Mike Baber

Additional photography
David Jefferis
Peter Mackertich

Acknowledgements
We wish to thank the following individuals and organizations for their assistance and for making available information and photographs from their collections.
Associated Newspapers Ltd
Columbia Warner Distributors Ltd
Gerry Anderson Productions Ltd
Federico Arboro Mella
Keith Wilson
Radio Times Hulton Picture Library
Royal Geographical Society

First published in 1977 by Usborne Publishing Ltd
20 Garrick Street, London WC2E 9BJ

© 1977 Usborne Publishing Ltd

Reprinted 1979

The material in this book is also published as three books, **All about Monsters, All about Ghosts** and **All about UFO's** in Usborne Publishing's World of the Unknown series.

Printed in Belgium by Henri Proost, Turnhout, Belgium.

ALL ABOUT MONSTERS

About this book

This book is for anyone who has wondered about the mysterious things thought to happen in the outer reaches of the known world.

Strange beasts have been reported lurking in mountains, forests, lakes and oceans. Are the accounts of them to be believed?

Many people say they have had contact with the spirits of the dead. Do ghosts really exist?

Over 100,000 people claim to have spotted flying saucers. Can they all be wrong? Or are UFO's patrolling the Earth's atmosphere at this very moment?

This book is your guide to the unknown. Perhaps when you have read it, you will have some answers to these questions.

Contents

The word "monster" is used to describe any strange creature. It comes from the Latin word *monstrum* (an omen). At one time people thought that the appearance of an abnormal creature was an omen, or warning, of an unusual event. The word is most often used, however, of things that are particularly big, fierce, or frightening.

There have been monsters of various kinds throughout history. Some actually existed, others were only thought to exist; some were created by story-tellers and others were a mixture of fact and fantasy. A few examples of monsters are shown on this page.

▲ Fifty thousand years ago, people in Europe hunted (or were hunted by) this terrifying, real-life monster. It is a *Smilodon* Sabre-tooth Cat. Its dagger-like teeth, used for stabbing its victims, grew up to 15 centimetres long.

▲ Before people understood the real causes for natural disasters, such as earthquakes, they often believed that monsters caused them. In the Middle East, an evil, smoke-like monster called a Jinn, shown above, was blamed for creating sandstorms.

Aepyornis's **egg**

Hen's egg

▲ Many of the monsters of myth and legend have a factual basis. The giant bird called the Roc in the story of Sinbad the Sailor was probably based on the discovery of the giant eggs of this flightless bird. It is an *Aepyornis*, a giant ostrich that lived on the island of Madagascar, off the coast of Africa, until it became extinct in the 1660's. The bird must have been known to Arab traders and to sailors, who used to store rum in the bird's empty egg-shells.

▲ People tried to please and soothe the monsters in various ways. Hai Ho Shang, a terrible Chinese sea monster, could be calmed by a sailor performing a dance to the beat of a gong It could also be frightened away by the smell of burning feathers which it hated.

▲ Today, most of the world has been mapped and photographed, but there are still a few unknown regions, such as the ocean depths. While they remain unexplored, there is still a chance that monsters, like the one above, may lurk somewhere.

Ancient Greece

The Ancient Greeks believed that the world was controlled by gods, goddesses and other supernatural creatures. Some of these creatures were monsters, half-human and half-beast or strange combinations of different animals.

The Greeks told tales about these gods and monsters and their encounters with humans. Often human heroes had to battle or outwit the monsters.

One of the most famous stories is *The Odyssey*, a long poem composed by Homer, which tells of the adventures of the Greek warrior Odysseus, as he sailed home from the battle of Troy.

▲ The Greeks were excellent sailors who explored and colonized the land around the Mediterranean Sea. The red area on the map shows the lands that they knew. Beyond these, lay unexplored regions where they thought that monsters might live.

▲ The Sirens were beautiful women with birds' wings and claws, who lured sailors to their island home with their hypnotic songs. When the sailors were shipwrecked on the rocks, the Sirens tore their victims to shreds and then devoured them.

One-eyed giants

Odysseus and his crew met many monsters on their journey. Once, they came to the island of the Cyclops— huge, one-eyed giants, who lived as shepherds. Odysseus and his men went ashore and took refuge in a cave which turned out to be the home of Polyphemus, the fiercest Cyclops of all. Polyphemus came back to the cave with his sheep. He blocked the entrance with a huge boulder.

Trapped inside the giant's lair, Odysseus had no choice but to approach Polyphemus and ask for his mercy. Instead of welcoming them, the giant seized two of the men and ate them. The next morning, he devoured two more and left the survivors shut inside the cave.

The Cyclops is blinded

Odysseus set to work on a plan of escape. He found a stake and sharpened its tip. That night, when the giant slept, Odysseus held the stake in the fire until it was red-hot, and then drove it into Polyphemus's only eye, blinding him. The giant roared with anger and pain, but could not see the men to kill them.

In the morning, Polyphemus rolled away the stone to let his flock out. To make sure that the men were not sneaking past, the giant felt the back of each sheep as it went by. But Odysseus tricked him once again. He and his men clung to the sheeps' bellies as they trotted out of the cave. In this way, they managed to escape from the Cyclops undetected.

Minotaur and Medusa

Among the most gruesome monsters of Greek legend are the Minotaur and the Gorgons. The Minotaur was a man with the head of a ferocious bull. The Gorgons were three sisters with snakes growing from their heads instead of hair. Any human who dared look them in the face was instantly turned to stone. Medusa was the most well known of the Gorgons.

Monster of the Labyrinth

The wife of King Minos of Crete gave birth to a horrible monster called the Minotaur. It was part bull, part man, and was imprisoned in a maze called the Labyrinth. The maze was so cleverly made that no-one could find their way out of it.

The Minotaur ate only human flesh, so King Minos had to provide living victims to be fed to the monster. Among the victims were fourteen young people that Athens had to pay in tribute to Crete yearly because the Athenians had been defeated in battle. Theseus, the son of the King of Athens, volunteered to go as one of the victims and to put an end to this cruel sacrifice by killing the monster.

The end of the Minotaur

When Theseus arrived in Crete, Ariadne, the daughter of Minos, fell in love with him. She gave him a ball of thread to help him with his task.

When Theseus entered the Labyrinth, he carefully tied one end of the thread to the entrance, and unwound the ball behind him as he went into the maze. When Theseus finally reached the hungry monster, he fought with it and managed to kill it. Then, by rewinding the thread, he was able to find his way out of the Labyrinth and rejoin Ariadne.

Medusa of the Gorgons

Medusa was once a beautiful woman, but the goddess Athena hated her and changed her into a monster. She became so hideous that anyone who looked at her was turned to stone.

A Greek hero called Perseus was set the impossible task of bringing back Medusa's head to win his bride. To help him, Athena gave Perseus a helmet which made him invisible, and a shining shield.

Armed with these, Perseus approached Medusa while she slept. Taking care not to look at her face, but only her reflection in the shield, he cut off Medusa's head and avoided being turned to stone.

Grendel

The Old English poem *Beowulf* is another story of a monster-slaying hero. This epic poem was written about 750 A.D in northern England, but the poet remains unknown.

The poem tells the story of the hero Beowulf and his three battles with monsters. In his youth, Beowulf gains fame by killing the monster Grendel, who has been terrorizing the hall of King Hrothgar. Then he kills Grendel's mother, an even fiercer monster, when she tries to avenge her son.

In old age, Beowulf single-handedly fights and kills a dragon that is destroying his people, but he dies as a result of his wounds.

▲ Although Beowulf is thought to be a fictional character, there is some historical basis for the poem. King Hrothgar was a real fifth century Danish King, whose stronghold was located on the island of Zealand, off the mainland of Denmark.

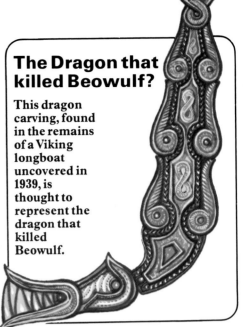

The Dragon that killed Beowulf?

This dragon carving, found in the remains of a Viking longboat uncovered in 1939, is thought to represent the dragon that killed Beowulf.

The monster who hated music and dancing

Grendel was, in the words of the poem, a "mighty, monstrous fiend", who lived in the marshes near the stronghold of a Danish king called Hrothgar.

The King built a new banqueting hall for feasting. Every night, in his lair in the marshes, Grendel could hear the sounds of music and dancing coming from the hall. More than anything, the monster hated the sound of happiness and rejoicing.

Grendel's savage attack
One night, after the singing had stopped, Grendel stole across the fens and crept into the great hall. He found Hrothgar's men lying asleep on the floor. He snatched thirty men and returned to his lair to devour them. Greedy for more human flesh, he raided the hall the next night and every night after that, until few of Hrothgar's men remained alive, and the hall stood empty.

Beowulf fights the monster
Beowulf, leader of a people called the Geats, was a great warrior, and when he heard of Grendel, he wanted to test his strength against the monster. He came to King Hrothgar and boasted that he could kill Grendel. A feast was held in the hall to attract the monster. When Grendel arrived, Beowulf wrestled with him for hours, until he managed to tear out one of Grendel's arms. The monster crept back to his lair to die.

Dragons!

Of all the incredible monsters of the world's mythologies, the dragon is the most terrifying and well-known. Stories about this giant flying reptile – which often breathes fire – are thousands of years old and come from nearly every country.

The name "dragon" comes from the ancient Greek word for serpent. In medieval tales the word "worm" was used for both serpents and dragons.

Some dragons are really just large serpents, but other dragons look almost like dinosaurs. This is very strange because the legends about dragons were invented long before any one knew of the existence of dinosaurs.

Dragons East and West

Although there are dragons in both Eastern and Western mythology, they are quite different in appearance and behaviour. In Chinese mythology, dragons are usually friendly and bring good fortune. Although they are often wingless, they can fly.

Western dragons are dark, ugly, fire-breathing serpents with wings. They have always been thought of as evil and so many stories tell of heroes who try to destroy them. St George is probably the most famous dragon-slayer. According to the legend, he came to a place which was terrorized by a dragon that demanded to be fed young maidens. St George fought and killed the dragon and rescued the beautiful maiden.

Some dragons had as many as seven heads.

Dragons of Western legends usually live in caves or underwater. They often guard a vast hoard of treasure.

Dragons can have either two or four legs with the claws of an eagle.

The heraldic dragon on shields and coats-of-arms has: a wolf's head, a serpent's body, a bat's wings, an eagle's talons and a barbed tongue and tail. It is officially known as "dragonée".

The dragon story

▲ Britain has many legends about dragons. One story tells of a ferocious battle between a red and a white dragon. They were finally captured when asleep and were buried in the Welsh mountains. The red dragon became a symbol of war, and it can still be seen on the Welsh flag.

▲ In Norse myths, dragons guarded the burial mounds of warriors. Because the dragon was a symbol of war, Vikings painted dragons on their shields and carved dragons' heads on the prows of their warships. This dragon carving was found in a Viking burial site in Norway.

▲ In Chinese mythology, dragons were rarely evil. They were the companions of the gods and cruised through the heavens, gathering clouds and rain. Dragons were believed to control the weather and especially the rains which helped crops to grow. People tried to

Dragons' wings are like those of a giant bat.

Dragons have scaly skin like snakes or crocodiles.

The aerodynamics of dragon flight

This medieval dragon's wings are too small for it to fly in anything but short hops. Its wings are also set at the wrong angle – they flap forwards – which would result in the creature flying backwards!

please the dragons so that there would be a good harvest. If the dragons were angered, they could cause a flood, a drought or an eclipse. Even today, people fly dragon kites and carry paper dragons (shown above) in the New Year's parade to bring good luck.

▲ In 1912 a report was published which announced the discovery of a kind of "dragon" living on the island of Komodo in Indonesia. For years, pearl fishermen, the only people visiting the uninhabited island, had told stories of a giant land crocodile on Komodo that ate pigs and goats. The reports were so insistent that finally a zoological expedition was sent to investigate. The "dragons" turned out to be an unknown species of Giant Monitor Lizard, which grows up to three metres long. The Komodo Dragon is the biggest lizard on earth.

More dragons....

The Shaggy Beast's deadly arsenal

Dragons caused vast destruction by spitting flames and with their deadly teeth and claws.
The monster in this story was equipped with an amazing range of other weapons as well.

In the Middle Ages a furry dragon, called the Shaggy Beast, terrorized a small, peaceful village in France. It raided farms, devoured children and young girls and ruined crops. Finally, a young man, seeking revenge for his dead sweetheart, cut the dragon's tail in two. This was the only place where it could be wounded and so it died.

Deadly stingers could be fired from its fur to maim and kill the creature's enemies.

Searing flames that destroyed crops

Tricks of dragon-slaying

Dragon-killing was always difficult and dangerous. Often the dragon-slayers had to use tricks to help them, as in this tale of the Lambton Worm from the north of England.

One Sunday, when he should have been in church, young John Lambton, the heir to Lambton Castle, was fishing in the River Wear. He caught a hideous worm, hauled it onto land and threw it into a well to get rid of it. He forgot about the worm and soon after went abroad for seven years.

But the worm grew enormous and crept out of the well. It lay coiled around a rock in the middle of the river. At night, it crawled up on land and terrorized the countryside, killing people and livestock. Many attempts were made to kill the worm, but whenever it was chopped to pieces, the pieces grew back together again!

When Lambton returned and learned what had happened, he was determined to destroy the monster. He went to consult a witch, who told him to stud his armour with razor-sharp spikes and to fight the monster in mid-stream.

The worm appeared and Lambton attacked it with his sword. When the monster coiled itself around him, the razor-studded armour cut it to shreds. The pieces of the worm fell into the river and were swept away before they could join up again.

Discovering dinosaurs

Until the 19th century, no-one had the slightest idea that dinosaurs once lived on earth. The first remains of such an animal were unearthed in a quarry in Oxfordshire, England, in 1822. The creature to which the remains belonged was named *Megalosaurus*, which means "big lizard". (The word "dinosaur" means "terrible lizard").

Since then, over 800 fossils of the long-extinct dinosaurs have been discovered and studied. We now know that although some of the dinosaurs were fierce hunters, there were many others which were harmless plant-eaters.

Iguanodon is unearthed

In 1822, the remains of a plant-eating dinosaur were found in England by Dr and Mrs Gideon Mantell. The Mantells were travelling in Sussex, and made a stop near Cuckfield so that Dr Mantell could attend to a patient. Mrs Mantell wandered into the trees nearby, and noticed some teeth sticking out of the ground. She took them to show to her husband.

Although he was a keen fossil collector, he had never seen anything like them before. He sent them to an expert in Paris to find out which animal they came from.

Iguanodon gets its name

The expert identified them as being the upper front teeth of a rhinoceros. Dr Mantell refused to believe this, and took the fossils to the Museum in the Royal College of Surgeons, in London. There, they were compared with the teeth of a South American iguana, a type of lizard. They were much larger than the iguana's teeth, but the similarity was unmistakable. Dr Mantell decided, therefore, to call his discovery *"Iguanodon"*, which means "iguana tooth".

Reconstructing the monster

Dr Mantell spent five years searching for more evidence of *Iguanodon*. Eventually he found part of a skeleton, and from it a life-size model was built and displayed. It was not until 1878 that the model was found to be completely wrong.

In that year, some Belgian coal miners found a pit into which 31 *Iguanodon* had fallen to their deaths millions of years before. Their skeletons helped scientists to reconstruct a more accurate model of *Iguanodon*.

▲ In 1851, life-size models of dinosaurs were exhibited in London. They were based on fossils, and *Iguanodon* (above) was based on Dr Mantell's evidence. It was mistakenly shown walking on four legs. The horn placed on its snout was really a thumb-bone.

▼ Before the exhibition, a dinner was held inside the model's stomach. Twenty-one scientists and other guests drank a toast to *Iguanodon's* restoration. Over the page, you can see what this reptile really looked like and how it would have stood.

Lords of the world

For 140 million years, dinosaurs were the most important reptiles on earth. More than 800 different kinds of dinosaurs developed during this period and they lived all over the world.

All the information we have about dinosaurs comes from studying their fossils. Some of these are bones and teeth that have, over the ages, turned into stone. Others include footprints, which tell us how dinosaurs stood and moved, patterns made on rocks by their skin, and fossils of dinosaur eggs. Scientists have even found the fossilized contents of dinosaurs' stomachs!

How the dinosaurs developed

The first true dinosaurs were flesh-eating reptiles. One of the earliest was *Ornithosuchus* (see chart below). It had clawed feet and powerful jaws to kill its prey. Scientists think that all the large flesh-eating dinosaurs which appeared later, developed from *Ornithosuchus*.

The smaller flesh-eating dinosaurs probably developed from the long-necked, slender *Coelophysis*. It could move its head quickly to snap up small animals, such as insects.

Plant-eating dinosaurs

Plant-eating dinosaurs developed later. Some species, like *Apatosaurus* (see chart below), grew to an enormous size. They became too heavy to walk upright, and moved along slowly on all fours. The biggest of all was *Brachiosaurus*, weighing 100 tonnes and standing over 12 metres tall–more than twice the height of a giraffe.

Dinosaurs with armour

Later, some of the plant-eating dinosaurs grew rows of bony plates on their backs to protect them from the flesh-eaters. The largest was *Stegosaurus* (see chart below), which weighed nearly two tonnes.

Another group grew flat bones on their bodies that covered them rather like a tortoise's shell. *Scolosaurus* (see right) was one of these.

Duck-billed and horned dinosaurs

There were hundreds of varieties of hadrosaurs, or duck-billed dinosaurs, such as *Anatosaurus* (see next page). They had flat, duck-like mouths containing rows of tightly-packed teeth. Some grew horny crests on their heads.

The horned dinosaurs, like *Triceratops*, were the last group to appear and develop.

The end of the dinosaurs

No-one knows why the dinosaurs died out. Some people think that the plant-eating dinosaurs could not adapt to the new vegetation that was developing at that time. When they died, the flesh-eaters had no prey left.

Other people believe that the dinosaurs died out because of a change in the earth's climate, bringing cold winters. Before this, the earth had been warm all the year round, but now the dinosaurs lost all their body heat in the winter, and could not warm up again when the summers came. Many other theories have been put forward, but the puzzle is still unsolved.

Triceratops had three sharp horns, each up to a metre long, which it used to defend itself against flesh-eating dinosaurs. The entire animal was 11 metres long and weighed 8.5 tonnes.

Scolosaurus was a 3.5 tonne armoured dinosaur, protected by bony plates on its body. Its clubbed tail had two spikes for swiping attackers.

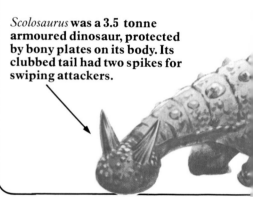

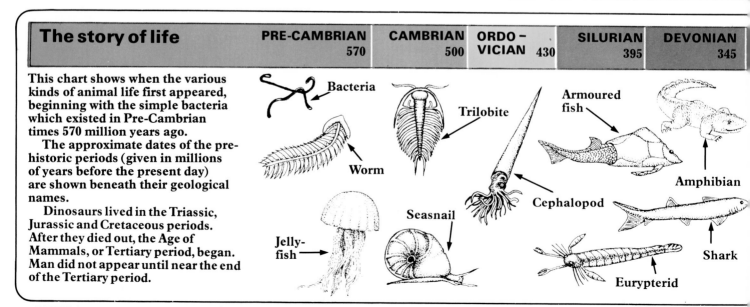

The story of life

	PRE-CAMBRIAN 570	CAMBRIAN 500	ORDO-VICIAN 430	SILURIAN 395	DEVONIAN 345

This chart shows when the various kinds of animal life first appeared, beginning with the simple bacteria which existed in Pre-Cambrian times 570 million years ago.

The approximate dates of the prehistoric periods (given in millions of years before the present day) are shown beneath their geological names.

Dinosaurs lived in the Triassic, Jurassic and Cretaceous periods. After they died out, the Age of Mammals, or Tertiary period, began. Man did not appear until near the end of the Tertiary period.

Bacteria

Trilobite

Armoured fish

Worm

Cephalopod

Amphibian

Jellyfish

Seasnail

Shark

Eurypterid

NOTE–The creatures shown on these two pages are not drawn to the same scale.

The long-tailed *Rhamphorhynchus* lived in the Jurassic period. It had long, sharp teeth for catching fish.

Spinosaurus lived in a very hot region. It had a "sail" of skin, held up by spines which grew from its back-bone. This increased the surface area of its body, and probably helped it to cool down more quickly if it overheated.

Spiky thumb, at first thought to be a horn on *Iguanodon's* snout.

Pterosaurs were flying reptiles. They had leathery wings and furry bodies, like huge bats. Like the dinosaurs, they died out towards the end of the Cretaceous period.

This is the modern view of what *Iguanodon* looked like. Unlike the 19th-century model, it is now known to have walked on its hind legs.

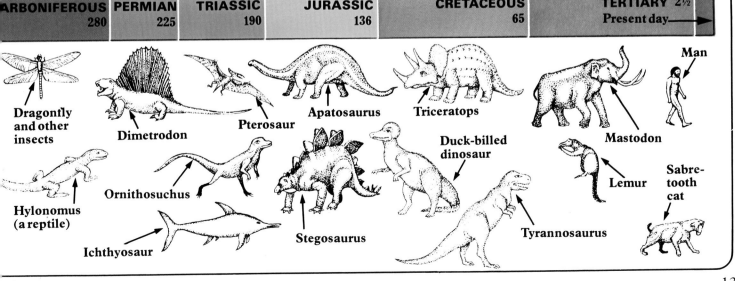

ARBONIFEROUS	PERMIAN	TRIASSIC	JURASSIC	CRETACEOUS	TERTIARY 2½
280	225	190	136	65	Present day

Dragonfly and other insects

Dimetrodon

Pterosaur

Apatosaurus

Triceratops

Man

Mastodon

Hylonomus (a reptile)

Ornithosuchus

Stegosaurus

Duck-billed dinosaur

Lemur

Sabre-tooth cat

Ichthyosaur

Tyrannosaurus

The fiercest beast to walk the Earth?

Tyrannosaurus rex is the largest flesh-eating dinosaur yet discovered. It roamed the earth 70 million years ago, in the Cretaceous period of prehistory. Its name means "king of the tyrant reptiles", and this huge beast must have had few enemies.

Standing erect on its massive back legs, it was 6 metres tall, about 15 metres long and weighed more than 8 tonnes. Its greatest handicap was its tiny brain.

In spite of its powerful legs, *Tyrannosaurus* was too heavy to run fast, and the smaller, lighter dinosaurs could easily outpace it. Its clawed feet were used for killing and tearing its prey. Its front arms were so short that it probably only used them for picking its teeth, and for pushing itself off the ground after resting.

Its razor-sharp teeth were 15 centimetres long and could have sliced up the flesh of dead dinosaurs quite easily. One large meal would probably have lasted *Tyrannosaurus* several weeks, so it may have spent a lot of time resting and sleeping.

Gigantic killer

Tyrannosaurus rex, shown here to scale with a man, had a stiff tail which swept from side to side as the animal waddled along. The heavy tail helped *Tyrannosaurus* to balance itself, as the top half of its body was so massive.

The landscape of the late Cretaceous period looked similar to that of today's woodlands.

Tyrannosaurus was armed with thick, curved talons as well as blade-like teeth. The animal it is attacking is a duck-billed dinosaur.

An agile *Ornithomimus* running off with a piece of flesh.

Tyrannosaurus ate whatever it could catch. Slow-moving, plant-eating dinosaurs, like the duck-billed *Anatosaurus* on the left, were a typical prey. They lived in large groups as a defence against the flesh-eaters. Group defence is used by lots of creatures. Staying in a group, an animal is less likely to be caught by a predator than if it lives by itself.

Serpents in the sea

Oceans cover more than two-thirds of the earth's surface, and in places reach a depth of eleven kilometres. This underwater world has not yet been thoroughly explored, so it is possible that unknown monsters exist there.

Between the 17th century and the present day, there have been hundreds of detailed sightings of terrifying creatures at sea. These are most often described as giant squid and octopuses (see pages 18-19) or as "sea serpents".

Reports of sea serpents say they look like smooth snakes, but they are many times larger than the biggest snakes on earth: the longest seem to be about 200 metres.

They are said to be yellow or mottled brown in colour, often with seaweed-like manes. Their heads can be up to three metres long, equipped with curving teeth. They seem to have neither fins nor limbs, and they twist and turn through the water like snakes.

▲ In the 16th century, when this map was made, little was known about creatures that lived in remote areas of the globe. Map-makers decorated their maps with imaginary beasts.

▶ The serpent found by *Monongahela's* crew may have looked like this. Mariners' tales, often exaggerated by retelling, are the main source of information about sea monsters.

Monongahela's monster

In 1852, two whaling ships, the *Monongahela* and the *Rebecca Sims*, from New Bedford (see map on right), were sailing alongside each other in the Pacific. A look-out reported a whale off the port bow. The master of the *Monongahela*, **Captain Seabury**, launched three longboats to go after it.

As they drew near their prey, the sailors realized that they were dealing with something much more fierce than any whale. Seabury nevertheless decided to tackle it, and thrust a harpoon deep into the creature's neck. It died within minutes, but not before sinking the other two longboats with its threshings

The sailors hauled in their amazing catch. The captain of the *Rebecca Sims* described it in the ship's log as a brownish-grey reptile at least 45 metres long. In its great jaws were dozens of sharp and curving teeth.

The body was too large to bring on board, so the head was cut off and preserved in a pickling vat aboard the *Monongahela*.

The monster is lost

The two ships then started back for their home port. The *Rebecca Sims* returned safely, but the other ship was never seen again. No trace of its crew, nor of the monster's head, was ever found. Only some wreckage was washed up, off the coast of Alaska.

The North Sea Terror

In 1881, a Scottish fishing boat, the *Bertie,* was 140 kilometres out in the North Sea. Suddenly, the crew noticed three humps breaking the surface of the water, and then part of a head draped with a growth that looked like seaweed. Two fierce eyes glared at the terror-stricken sailors.

The creature headed straight for the boat. The crew tried to drive it away, and one man fired a rifle at it. The "serpent" churned the water, almost capsizing the boat.

Fishing gear was thrown off the deck and two of the crew were pitched violently backwards into the hold.

The fishermen cut their lines and set sail for port, but the sea serpent continued to follow them. When night fell, the crew lost sight of the strange monster.

Panic in the fog

In 1962, off the Florida coast, an American Air Force raft, carrying five skin-divers, was swept out to sea in a storm. As the storm cleared, dense fog came down.

After they had been stranded for about an hour, they heard splashing and noticed a smell of dead fish, then a hissing noise. Suddenly, what looked like a brown, slimy neck, about four metres long, reared up out of the water. The creature's head was shaped like a sea turtle's. One diver saw the neck bend and the head dip into the water several times. The divers panicked and leapt into the sea. In the fog, they lost sight of one another. According to the only survivor, his comrades went under one by one, screaming in terror. They were never found.

Monongahela's route

NORTH AMERICA

New Bedford

Serpent sighted here

Whaling grounds

SOUTH AMERICA

Route of the *Monongahela*

The riddle of the Kraken

"Kraken" is an old Norse word used to describe giant sea creatures that mariners reported they had seen. They were said to be shaped like squid or octopuses, with many arms that could pluck men from ships, and even drag whole boats to the bottom of the sea.

Although many of the stories are exaggerated accounts, and were once thought to be only legends, there is now proof that giant squid do exist. Parts of squid and even whole bodies of enormous size have been found. They have been examined by experts in many different parts of the world.

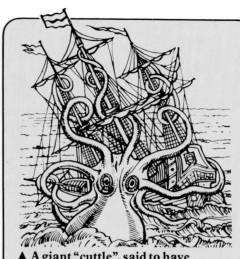

▲ A giant "cuttle", said to have wrapped its tentacles round the masts of an 18th-century slave ship.

Fight with a kraken

In 1873, two men and a boy were fishing in a rowing boat off the coast of Newfoundland, when one of the men stuck a boathook into a mass of floating wreckage. Suddenly, the "wreckage" jerked to life. It was an enormous sea monster. Two of its tentacles shot out to grasp the little boat.

The creature began to sink beneath the water, pulling the boat along with it. As the sea flooded around them, the boy grabbed an axe and hacked at the slithery tentacles. As he cut at them, the monster released a jet of black ink, withdrew and disappeared.

The fishermen reached the shore unharmed and took a piece of tentacle to show to a local naturalist called Moses

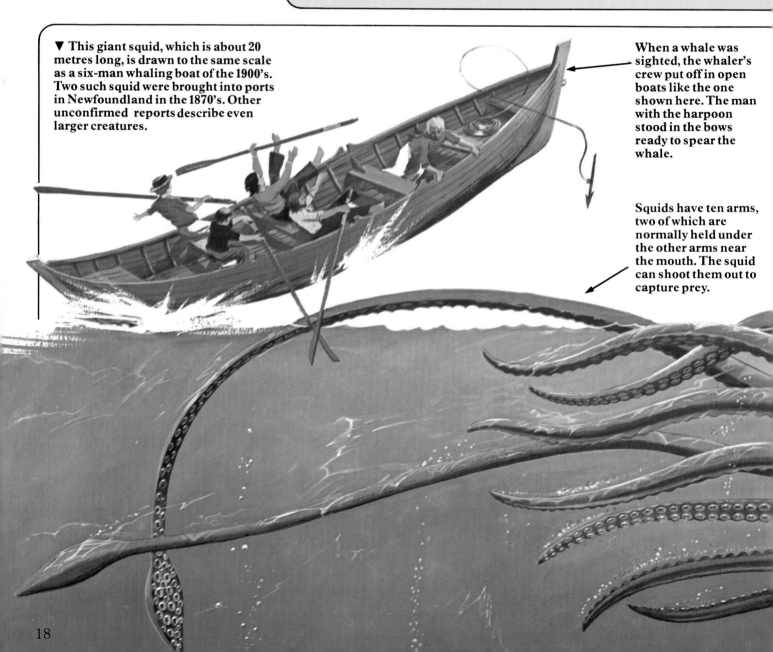

▼ This giant squid, which is about 20 metres long, is drawn to the same scale as a six-man whaling boat of the 1900's. Two such squid were brought into ports in Newfoundland in the 1870's. Other unconfirmed reports describe even larger creatures.

When a whale was sighted, the whaler's crew put off in open boats like the one shown here. The man with the harpoon stood in the bows ready to spear the whale.

Squids have ten arms, two of which are normally held under the other arms near the mouth. The squid can shoot them out to capture prey.

Harvey. He was amazed by the specimen, which was very tough and six metres long.

More proof is found

A month later, four other men brought Harvey a similar creature. They said they had been bringing in one of their nets, which had seemed very heavy. When they got it to the surface, they had seen a writhing mass of jelly, from which two fierce eyes had peered at them. They had battled with it until one of them killed it.

Moses Harvey bought the creature from the fishermen for ten dollars. He took several photographs of it and sent them off to London. There, scientists who examined it declared that it was a giant squid–one of the largest ever found.

In 1887, another giant squid was found, this time in New Zealand. Its body measured about 3 metres, and its tentacles were another 13 metres long. As recently as 1964, an 11-metre squid was found in the sea near La Coruna, in Spain.

Monsters of the deep

Even today, we do not know exactly how large squid can grow. One estimate is based on the size of marks found on the heads of some sperm whales (who eat mainly squid). These are scars left by the squids' suckers on the whales' skin. The whales seem to have fought with squid at least 25 metres long.

▲ A sea monster described in a book in the 16th century.

A squid is an invertebrate (an animal without a backbone), that is related to the octopus and the cuttlefish. Squid have circular suckers on each of their arms. As well as giant squid like this one, there are small ones, about 20 centimetres long.

Giant squid live in deep open water, but may come to the surface of the sea in search of food. Their diet includes shellfish and fish. They are pursued and eaten by toothed whales. Bodies of giant squid have been found in sperm whales' stomachs.

The squid can contract its body suddenly, forcing out a strong jet of water, which propels it backwards. It can also squirt out ink to confuse its enemies.

▲ Some people think that the idea of sea serpents arose from sightings of giant squid. If a squid was under the water, and raised one tentacle above the surface, as in this picture, this could appear to be a snake-like head and neck.

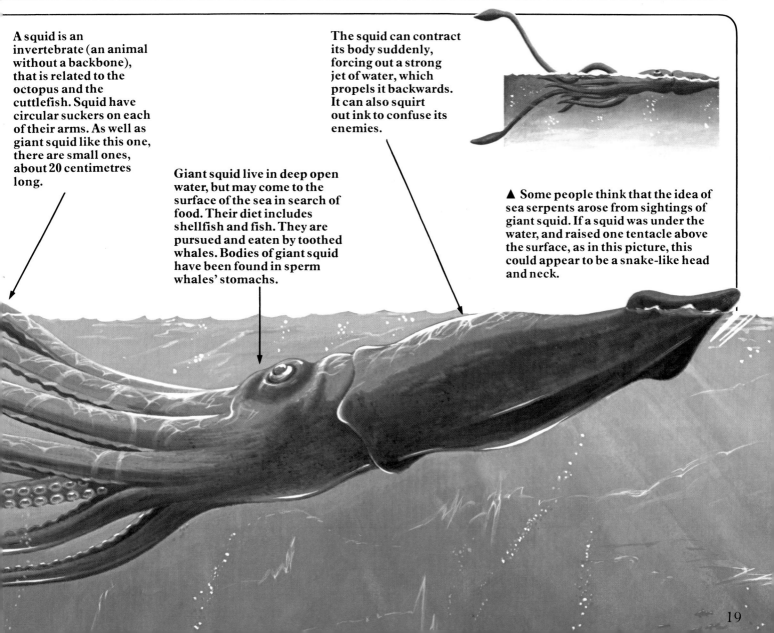

The Abominable Snowman...

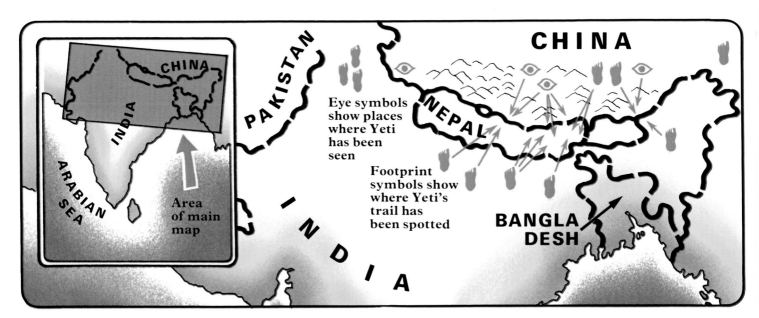

▲ This map shows the places where people claim to have seen Yetis or their tracks. Unidentified ape-like creatures have also been seen in other places, such as high in the Pamir mountains, north of Pakistan.

Over the last 100 years, reports have come in from many parts of the world of a man-like beast that walks upright and is covered in shaggy hair. These unknown animals have many names, but in the countries spanned by the Himalayan mountains, it is called the Yeti, or Abominable Snowman.

The reports differ, but many of them agree on the following features: the creature is about two metres tall when standing upright, and has a powerful body completely covered in reddish-brown hair. It has long arms that reach to its knees and a hairless face that looks like an ape's. It is said to be shy and not aggressive to humans.

It has been seen both in the forested areas on the lower slopes of the Himalayas and higher up, in the snowfields. It seems to be active mainly at night and is usually alone, although it has been seen in pairs. Some observers say that it eats goats and other mammals, while others say it is vegetarian. No-one has ever managed to capture or to photograph a Yeti.

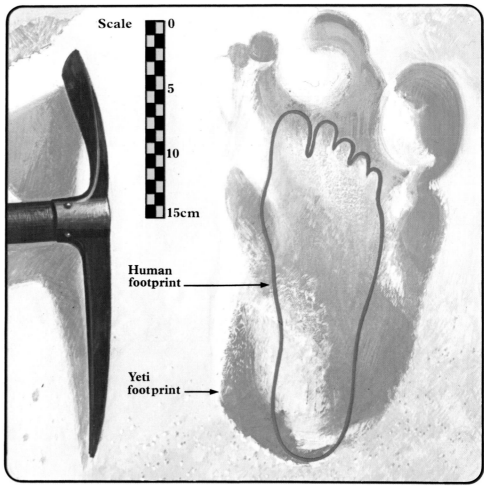

▲ In 1951, a British explorer, Eric Shipton, found a long set of Yeti footprints on the Menlung Glacier, near the border between Nepal and Tibet (now part of China). He took a photograph of them alongside an ice-pick handle. The prints were 33 cm long and 20 cm wide.

They clearly showed an unusually long, thick second toe. The tracks showed where the animal had jumped a crevasse, digging its toes deeply into the ice to prevent itself from falling. Whatever made the tracks looked as though it walked on two feet.

Encounters in the snow

In 1942, seven Polish prisoners escaped from a Soviet labour camp in Siberia. In his book which describes their journey, Slavomir Rawicz tells how they encountered two Yetis.

As the men crossed the Himalayas on their way to India, they saw two creatures on a rocky shelf about 90 metres away from them. Rawicz says they were nearly 2.5 metres tall and covered in long hair. They resembled apes or bears and shuffled about on the ledge for two hours while the men watched them. They showed no signs of fear, even though they were aware of the onlookers.

Although his report is one of the most detailed ever recorded, some people doubt that it is all true.

Yeti or spy?

During the Second World War, in 1941, a Soviet army doctor in the Caucasus was asked to examine a man thought to be a spy. The man had been found in the mountains.

"He was obviously a man", said the doctor, "because his entire shape was human. Yet he had shaggy hair two or three centimetres long all over his body. He stood before me like a proud giant but his eyes were dull and empty like the eyes of an animal. He was not a spy in disguise, but some kind of wild man".

A cliff-top sighting

A Russian scientist, Dr Pronin, of Leningrad University, claims to have glimpsed the Yeti in 1958. Dr Pronin was studying glaciers in the Pamirs when he saw a figure outlined on top of a cliff about 400 metres away from him. He described the creatures as thick-set, long-armed and covered in reddish-grey hair.

"It walked out of a cave for about 200 metres or so, and then vanished over the edge of the cliff", reported Dr Pronin. He said that the creature was known to the local villagers as "the wild man".

...and its cousin, the Sasquatch

The Sasquatch is a man-like beast similar to the Yeti, and is said to live in the remote forests of North America. This name, which means "hairy giant", was given to it by the North American Indians, but it is also known as Bigfoot.

Since the first report of this creature by a white man in 1811, there have been hundreds of sightings. Bigfoot is usually described as being over two metres tall, and footprints 40 centimetres long have been found. As yet, however, no-one has managed to prove Bigfoot's existence.

Among other things, Bigfoot is supposed to have interrupted picnics, grappled with moving cars, and actually walked into people's homes. A lumberjack named Albert Ostman claimed that in 1924 he was kidnapped by a whole family of "near human hairy beasts" in British Columbia but managed to escape.

The hungry Sasquatch

The Sasquatch is said to live on roots, berries and leaves in the summer, and on any sort of meat (from rats to cows) in the winter. This diet is similar to that of the bears that live in North America. The creatures is also reported to have stolen fish, doughnuts and, on one occasion, chocolate.

▲ This map shows that most Sasquatch sightings occur in the mountainous regions near the Pacific coast. The black dots show places where Sasquatch has been sighted or prints found.

► In 1967, Roger Patterson, a keen Bigfoot tracker, went to Bluff Creek Valley in California to look for signs of the monster. He claims to have come across a female Bigfoot, and to have taken a film of her. One frame from the film is shown here, with the Bigfoot arrowed. Professor John Napier, an expert on the human body and the mechanics of walking, studied the film and said that it was probably a hoax.

Confusing footprints

Many people have said that the Sasquatch footprints were not made by an unknown beast at all, but were those of various well-known animals, or of human beings. The feet of some of these animals are shown here, along with a human foot and a reconstruction of a Sasquatch foot, based on footprints found. The human foot looks most like the Sasquatch foot, in shape if not in size.

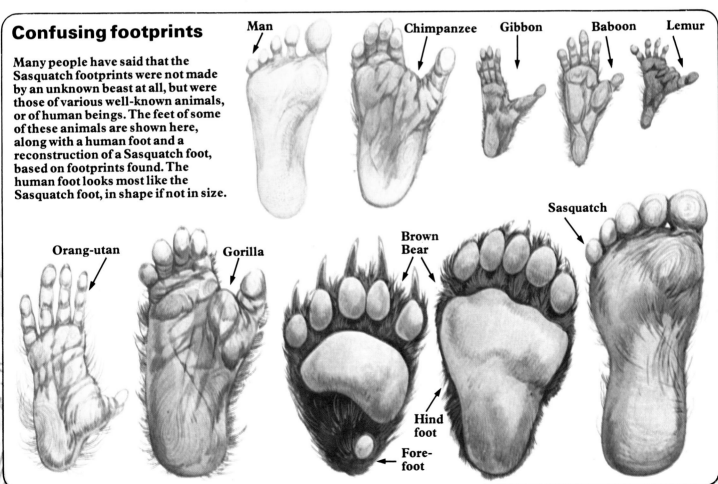

Man

Chimpanzee

Gibbon

Baboon

Lemur

Orang-utan

Gorilla

Brown Bear

Sasquatch

Hind foot

Fore-foot

Monsters in the loch

Loch Ness is one of three lochs (loch is a Gaelic word which means lake) that form a chain across the Highlands of Scotland.

The shores of the lake plunge steeply into peat-stained, icy waters up to 297 metres deep.

For a thousand years there have been reports of huge creatures swimming in the loch. But nobody has caught one, and even recent underwater photographs only show very blurred images.

Some people believe that the monsters of the loch—if they exist— are prehistoric animals which were trapped in the loch during the Ice Ages.

This is what a lot of people think the Loch Ness Monster might look like. Fossils of similar creatures, called *Elasmosaurs*, have been found. They lived in the oceans 70 million years ago.

The monster's diet could include salmon, pike, eels and plankton, all of which live in the loch.

Many spotters agree that the creature's neck is long and thin, with a small snake-like head.

Photographs of a diamond-shaped flipper-like object were taken by underwater cameras in 1972.

Maybe they arrived like this....

1

▲ There have been several Ice Ages, when the land was covered with thick ice. Steep-sided valleys like Loch Ness were gouged out of the earth by slow-moving mountains of ice. Wooly Mammoths like the one above lived during these Ice Ages.

2

▲ When the ice melted 12,000 years ago, the sea level rose. Loch Ness, along with other similar valleys, was flooded. It became a long, thin arm of the sea, rather like the fiords of Norway. Various sea creatures came to live in the newly-formed salt-water inlets.

3

▲ The land was no longer crushed by billions of tonnes of ice, so it gradually rose. Eventually Loch Ness was cut off from the North Sea. The sea creatures still in the loch either adapted to their new life in the lake, or they died out.

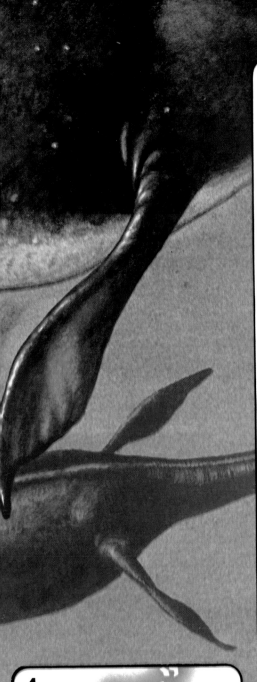

Some famous sightings

The earliest written reference to a monster in Loch Ness was in the diaries of St Columba, an English missionary in Scotland, in about AD 565. He writes of attending the burial of a man who had been bitten to death by a water beast while swimming.

An underwater shock

Much later, in 1880, a diver, Duncan McDonald, was sent to examine a sunken ship at the western end of the loch. Within minutes of reaching the wreck, he made frantic signals to be brought to the surface.

Witnesses said that he came out trembling violently. He claimed to have seen an enormous animal lying on a shelf of rock: "It was an odd-looking beastie", he said, "like a huge frog". He refused to dive in Loch Ness ever again.

The Mackays meet the monster

In 1933 the first motor road was built alongside the loch. In April of that year Mr and Mrs John MacKay were driving along the road when Mrs MacKay noticed a disturbance on the surface of the loch. At first she thought it was made by fighting ducks. Suddenly the splashing was replaced by a large V-shaped wake made by something moving at great speed.

When the wake was about 400 metres from shore, two large humps appeared. They moved in a line, with the rear one looking larger than the front one. The MacKays got out of their car and watched "an enormous animal rolling and plunging" until it disappeared with a huge splash.

The monster on land

Since 1933, 3,000 people claim to have seen the monster, and it is interesting that many of them describe a V-shaped wake, terrific disturbance of the water surface, and several humps being visible.

Other accounts speak of large unidentified animals on land around the lakeside. In 1934, Arthur Grant was travelling by motorcycle on the road by the loch, when he saw the monster. He says it crossed the road in front of him in two bounds and disappeared into the water. It had small, flipper-like forelimbs and was about six metres long.

Danger on the loch

In 1960, the Lowrie family were on the loch in their motor yacht, when they saw a form that looked like "two ducks... and a neck-like protrusion breaking surface". Mr Lowrie only had time to take four photographs, one of which showed a V-shaped wake, before changing course to avoid a collision with the creature.

A year earlier, the monster had been seen by a couple who were driving their car on the southern side of the loch. They said that a huge animal, with a long neck and a small head, emerged from the bracken at the side of the road, carrying a dead lamb in its mouth. Then it plunged into the loch and disappeared.

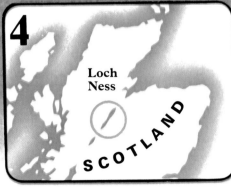

▲ This map shows Loch Ness as it is today—a narrow lake 39 kilometres long, cut off from the sea. When the floor and sides of the lake were studied, with equipment normally used for detecting shipwrecks on the seabed, large underwater caves were found.

▲ This photograph was taken by a doctor, Colonel Robert Wilson, in 1934. He also took a picture of the head as it sank into the water. The ripples on the surface seem to indicate that there is a body under the water as well as the head and neck that are visible.

▲ The best-known landmark of Loch Ness is the ruin of Castle Urquahart. The castle is half-way along the northern shore and has proved to be the most popular spot from which to catch a glimpse of the monster.

Scientists investigate Loch Ness

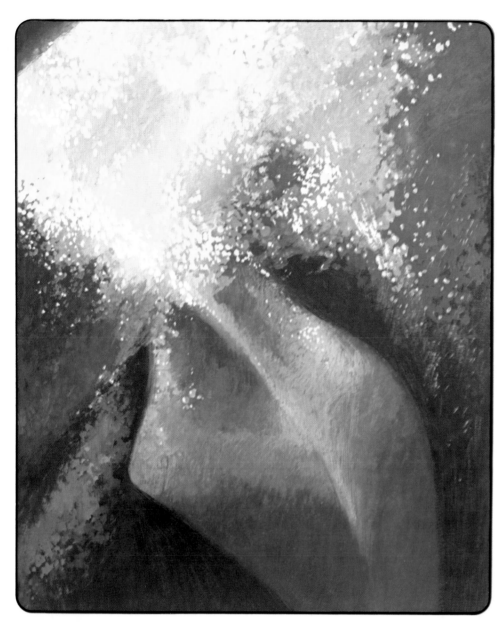

▲ In 1938, a fish like the one above was caught off the coast of South Africa. It was a *Coelacanth,* and scientists thought that it had been extinct for 70 million years. Perhaps the Loch Ness Monster will also prove to be a survivor of the past, but as yet, no-one has proof.

◀ This picture is based on a photograph taken in 1972 at the bottom of the loch by an American team. It shows a diamond-shaped flipper, apparently attached to the side of an animal. The flipper was reckoned to be about two metres long.

▶ This submarine, the Vickers Oceanic *Pisces,* was used to try and track down the monster in Loch Ness in 1969. It had a sonar screen, but did not collect any definite evidence about the monster. Another submarine, the *Viperfish,* had no success either.

For the monster-hunters of Loch Ness, there are many problems. Firstly, the loch is too large to be kept under constant watch. Thick mists often cover the surface, and under the water it is very hard to see anything clearly, because of particles of peat in the water.

People are constantly trying out new methods of recording evidence of large animals in the loch. The photographs taken by an American team in 1972 and 1975 caused a sensation when they were published. To many people, they were proof of the monster's existence. Other people were not so sure.

The first underwater photographs

In 1972, an American team at Loch Ness managed to take some underwater photographs. One picture appeared to be of an animal's flipper. Others showed what looked like a whole body.

The team used a camera which took a picture every time an electronic light flashed (about once every minute). It was linked to a sonar beam which bounced a pulse of high-pitched sound off objects and "blipped" their shape on to a screen in a boat above.

Even with such highly-developed equipment, the pictures were very murky and blurred. If the monster did exist, which many people still doubted, scientists disagreed over what kind of animal could be in the photographs.

Is the monster a prehistoric reptile?

The "flipper" above is unlike that of any known water creature. Some people suggest that it is rather like the limbs of some prehistoric reptiles. But the idea that "Nessie" is a relative of an early reptile has been rejected by some scientists.

They argue that the icy waters of a Scottish lake are no place for what was once a tropical marine reptile. They also say that if such an animal had survived, it would be more likely to have streamlined limbs, and not oar-shaped "flippers" as in the photo.

The argument about the monster's identity continued when the Americans produced a photo of a "head" in 1975. Some people argued that the horned "face" was more likely to be the prow of a sunken Viking ship, or even a piece of rotten wood.

It did not look like any animal that is known today, either living or extinct.

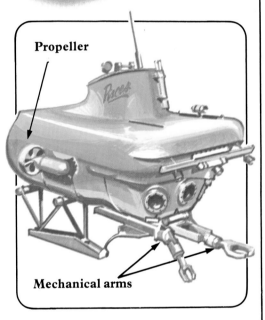

Propeller

Mechanical arms

Those who doubt the monster's existence ask why no dead bodies have been washed ashore, and no bones have been found. If, as is claimed, the loch has been a breeding colony for 12,000 years, surely there would be better evidence of the monster's presence by now? One reply to this suggests that the monsters eat stones to help their digestion; when they die, their bodies sink to the bottom of the loch.

Another possible explanation of some of the sightings was discovered in Norway on a lake said to contain monsters. Twice, people saw what looked like humps on the surface of the water, and rowed out to see the "Hvaler Serpent", as the monster was known. They found that the "humps" were nothing more than large mats of rotting vegetation, buoyed up by marsh gas.

Other lake monsters

Loch Ness is only one of about a dozen Scottish lakes that claims to have its own water monster. The number is just as high in Ireland. Similar animals have been reported swimming in freshwater lakes all over the world, and most of them before the Loch Ness monster was even heard of. A surprising number of these reports describe a creature with several humps and a small head on a long neck.

One Swedish monster, which is said to live in Lake Storsjö, was first heard of 80 years ago, when it chased two girls along the edge of the lake. The outraged locals made the cruel trap shown below for it. The creature appeared again, but fortunately was never caught in the trap.

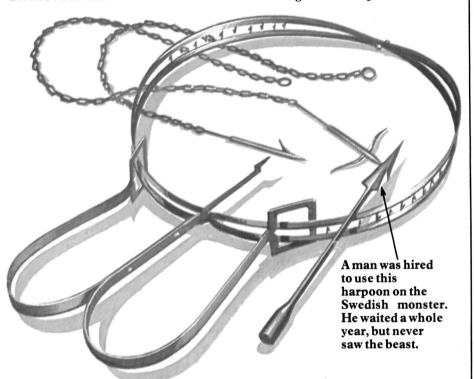

A man was hired to use this harpoon on the Swedish monster. He waited a whole year, but never saw the beast.

▼ The map below shows where some of the world's lake monsters are thought to live. They are usually associated with deep, remote lakes, surrounded by steep shores or mountains. Many of the monsters are said to churn up the surface of the water, and to look like upturned boats.

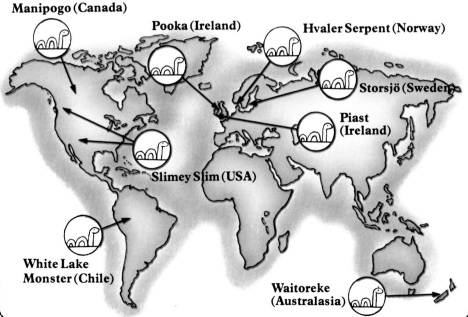

Manipogo (Canada)

Pooka (Ireland)

Hvaler Serpent (Norway)

Storsjö (Sweden)

Piast (Ireland)

Slimey Slim (USA)

White Lake Monster (Chile)

Waitoreke (Australasia)

Man-made monsters

Monsters have always been a popular subject for horror stories, and since the beginning of the century, they have also terrified and fascinated thousands of cinema audiences.

The task of making movie monsters as frightening as possible is the job of the "special effects" department in the film studio.

The monsters are usually either models (life-size or miniature) or actors wearing special costumes and make-up. The models are mechanized, so that they can move about, or else trick photography is used to make them look as though they are moving.

The first *King Kong* film appeared in 1933. It tells the story of a giant ape that is captured on a remote island and brought to New York. There it escapes and climbs to the top of the Empire State Building, clutching the screaming heroine. The monster finally meets its end when it plummets to the ground. The scenes of the ape were shot using six small models (made of rubber and rabbit fur) and a giant one of its head and shoulders, covered in bear skin.

Mechni-Kong (shown above) was built for a Japanese film, in which this colossal robot fights with the giant ape, King Kong. It is equipped with a death ray, mounted in its head.

In *Frankenstein*, the nameless monster is played by a heavily-made-up actor. In the story, Baron Frankenstein brings the monster to life by passing an electric current through its body.

For the film *Jaws*, about a giant shark, three full-size mechanical models were made. They were each packed with electronic and other equipment to make the different parts of the shark move.

In the film *2001 A Space Odyssey*, the "monster" is a computer called HAL 9000. The computer, which forms part of a spaceship on a mission to Jupiter, kills all but one of the crew and has to be destroyed. The film makes spectacular use of special effects to give the impression of travelling through space. The ship, shown above, was a model 18 metres long. A model was made to show even the planet Jupiter.

Many films have been made about Godzilla, an enormous prehistoric reptile that is aroused by an atomic explosion. In *Godzilla*, it destroys Tokyo, crunching up the city's trains (shown above).

A full-scale model of a giant squid was built for the film *20,000 Leagues Under the Sea* (made in 1954). The mechanical model weighed several tonnes, and had to be worked by a team of 16 men. At one point in the film, the squid attacks a submarine, called the *Nautilus*, and threatens to crush the vessel, along with her crew, with its enormous tentacles. This battle was filmed in a giant-sized water tank in the film studios.

In *The Mummy*, made in 1932, a mummified ancient Egyptian suddenly comes to life, leaves his tomb, and searches for a long-lost love. He murders and terrorizes people who stand in his way.

Making a monster

1

▲ These pictures show one way in which a "monster" can be made for films or television. First, the designer reads the script and sketches out his ideas. The monster in this case is a swamp creature, to be played by an actor in a special suit.

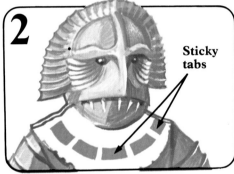

2

Sticky tabs

▲ The designer then discusses his ideas with the producer of the film. He decides to make the suit in separate pieces, stuck together with sticky tabs. This means that the costume can be used again if new parts, such as arms or a head, are added.

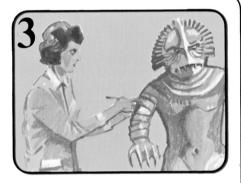

3

▲ The finished design is sent to a modelling unit. They first make a full-size clay model, scaled to fit the actor who will wear the suit. The clay model is then used to make a mould for the suit, which is cast in stretchy latex rubber.

4

▲ The rubber suit is then painted to make it look like rough skin. When the costume is finished, the actor tries it on for size. The zip up the back is hidden by a flap which blends in with the scaly "skin."

5 The finished creature

▶ Before the film can be made, the actor has to learn to move inside the suit, and to cope with any special problems, such as overheating, which the costume may give him. On the film set, the monster can be made to seem even more menacing by means of different camera angles, lighting and sound effects.

A dictionary of monsters

This dictionary of monsters includes some of the creatures in this book as well as others which have not been mentioned. Some of these beasts are mythical, while others really did exist.

AMPHISBAENA Legendary Greek beast, with a second head growing from its tail, that could move backwards and forwards. When one head was asleep, the other stayed awake to keep watch.

ANUBIS Ancient Egyptian god of the dead which had the body of a man and the head of a jackal.

BASILISK In Greek myth a creature whose poisonous touch or glance meant certain death. Only three things could kill it: a weasel, a cock crowing or the sight of itself in a mirror.

BERBALANGS Malaysians believed in these ghouls that looked like humans except for their wings and slit eyes. They dug up graves to eat dead bodies.

CERBERUS In Greek myths a ferocious watchdog that guarded the gates of hell. It was usually imagined as having three heads.

CHIMERA From Greek mythology a fierce monster with a lion's head, a goat's body and a serpent's tail. Sometimes it had three heads. It breathed fire.

CYCLOPS In Greek legends a tribe of one-eyed giants. See page 5.

DRAGONS Giant flying reptiles in tales from all over the world. See pages 8-10.

FRANKENSTEIN'S MONSTER An artificial man, made of parts of dead human bodies, which came to life. See page 28.

GANESHA Elephant-headed god of wisdom in Indian mythology. He had a fat, red human body, four arms and one large tusk. He rode on the back of a rat.

GRENDEL Flesh-eating monster who fought with the hero Beowulf. See page 7.

GRIFFIN Ancient mythical beast from the Middle East, which was as strong as a hundred eagles. It had the head, wings and talons of an eagle with the hind legs and tail of a lion. It made a nest of gold which it guarded fiercely.

HAI HO SHANG Legendary monster-fish with a shaven head which terrorized the South China Sea. It seized boats and drowned their crews.

HARPIES These creatures from Greek mythology had the head and breasts of a woman and the wings and claws of an eagle. They were foul-smelling, filthy beasts with monstrous appetites.

HYDRA Legendary Greek water serpent with many hideous human heads–stories vary from nine to one hundred heads. Each time a head was cut off, two new ones grew in its place.

KAPPA Legendary Japanese goblin with head of an ape, the body of a tortoise and a frog's legs. It lived in rivers, drowning and devouring people.

Griffin

KRAKEN Many-armed sea monster in Nordic legends. See pages 18-19.

KING KONG There are many popular horror films about this giant ape that rampaged through New York City. See page 28.

LAMBTON WORM Enormous dragon that terrorized an English village. See page 10.

LAMIAS These creatures of Greek myths were beautiful women from the waist upwards, but writhing serpents below the waist. With their beautiful whistling, they lured lost travellers to their den and ate them.

LOCH NESS MONSTER Large water creature reported to live in a Scottish Loch. See pages 24-27.

MAKARA Sea monster in Indian legends that was half-fish and half-mammal.

MANTICORE This weird mythological creature had a man's head with blue eyes and three rows of teeth. It had a lion's body and a scorpion's tail covered with spines that it could shoot like arrows.

MEDUSA In Greek legends a winged monster with snakes on her head. See page 6.

MINOTAUR Monster that was half-man and half-bull in Greek myths. See page 6.

MOA Giant, ostrich-like bird, over three metres tall, that lived in New Zealand until the 18th century. It defended itself by kicking its strong legs.

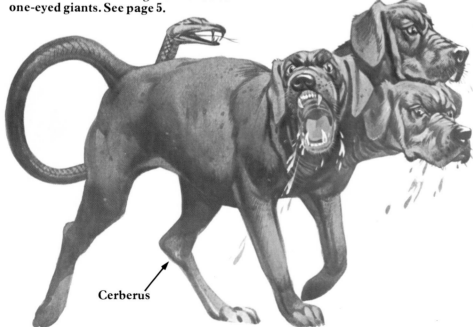

Cerberus

NAGAS These creatures of Indian mythology had snake-like bodies and human heads. They lived in palaces underground or in the water and had power over water–the seas, rivers and the rain.

NANDI BEAR Giant, flesh-eating bear which the people of the Nandi tribe in East Africa believe roams about after dark. It utters blood-curdling shrieks. Its footprints are four times the size of a human's.

NASNAS This horrific creature, in legends from the Middle East, is like a human being divided in half. It has half a face and body and only one arm and one leg.

OGRES These man-eating giants are common in legends of many countries. They are always very ugly, and in Japanese stories their bodies are red and blue and they have teeth like elephants' tusks.

PTERODACTYL Prehistoric flying reptiles that ate flesh. See page 13.

ROC This immense eagle-like bird, with a wingspan of thirty paces, appears in the Arabian legend of "Sinbad the Sailor". It was said to be so huge that it could eat an elephant, grasping the animal with its huge talons.

Scylla

Roc

SCYLLA In Greek mythology this six-headed serpent lived in a cave on the coast of Sicily. It snatched and devoured passing sailors.

SEA SERPENTS These large, unidentified monsters have been sighted in oceans all over the world. See pages 16-19.

SIMURG Giant mythical bird that lived on the highest mountain in ancient Persia.

SPHINX In Greek mythology this creature had a woman's head and breasts, a bird's wings and a lion's body and feet. She asked travellers riddles and if they could not answer, she devoured them.

SQUONK American folktales tell of this timid beast that lives in the forests of Pennsylvania. It cries because of its wart-covered, ill-fitting skin. If captured, it dissolves itself in tears.

TENGU Legendary Japanese monsters that were part human and part bird with huge claws and beaks. They had ferocious, glittering eyes.

THOTH The ancient Egyptian moon god, who had the body of a man, and the head of an ibis.

TYRANNOSAURUS REX This enormous prehistoric reptile was the largest, flesh-eating dinosaur that has yet been discovered. See pages 14-15.

WEREWOLVES Folktales from all over the world tell of people who are transformed into wolves at every full moon, when they kill and devour humans. The only way to kill them is with a silver bullet.

WYVERN Mythical flying serpent, much like a dragon but with an eagle's talons. Its sudden appearance was thought to herald the outbreak of war or plague.

YALE Horse-like monster with a goat's beard, a boar's tusk and an elephant's tail. It could swivel its huge horns from back to front when it was fighting its enemies.

YETI Huge, hairy man-like creature sometimes sighted in the Himalayas. See pages 20-21.

Werewolf

SALAMANDER Unlike the real lizard, this mythical reptile was said to live in fires. It had a deadly poisonous bite.

SASQUATCH Shaggy-haired, ape-like man which has been reported in remote regions of North America. See pages 22-23.

A monster quiz

Now that you have read about all the monsters, test your knowledge of them by trying to answer these questions. Then quiz your friends – see if they can do better.

The answers are printed below but are reversed to make cheating more difficult. All you need to do to read them is to hold this page upside down in front of a mirror.

1 How did Odysseus blind Polyphemus?
2 What part of the Shaggy Beast could be wounded?
3 What does 'dinosaur' mean?
4 How did Theseus escape from the Labyrinth after killing the Minotaur?
5 Up to how long were the teeth of the Sabre-tooth Cat?
6 Where and when were the first remains of the *Iguanodon* found?
7 What did *Tyrannosaurus rex* probably use its front arms for?
8 Which was the biggest of all dinosaurs, and how much did it weigh?
9 Where is the island of Komodo?
10 Who gave birth to the Minotaur?
11 Why was the Lambton Worm so difficult to kill?
12 How big were the Yeti footprints found by Eric Shipton in 1951?
13 What was the name of the master of the *Monongahela*?
14 Why did the Vikings paint dragons on their shields and carve dragons' heads on their warships?
15 How long had the *Coelacanth* been thought extinct when one was caught in 1938?
16 What was the purpose of the 'sail' on the back of the *Spinosaurus*?
17 In the Middle East what natural disaster was the Jinn blamed for?
18 Of which people was Beowulf the leader?
19 How did the Sirens lure sailors to their island home?
20 How tall was *Tyrannosaurus rex*?
21 When did Albert Ostman claim that he was kidnapped by a Sasquatch family?
22 How much of the earth's surface is covered by the oceans?
23 When was the poem "Beowulf" written?
24 In Chinese mythology, what were dragons believed to control?
25 In the story, how does Baron Frankenstein bring the monster to life?
26 What was used to try and track down the Loch Ness monster in 1969?
27 When was the first sighting of Bigfoot reported?
28 How many arms do squid have?
29 In which periods did the dinosaurs live?
30 What happened to anyone who looked at Medusa?
31 How many people claim to have seen the Loch Ness Monster since 1933?
32 What is the main source of information about sea monsters?
33 How could the Chinese monster Hai Ho Shang be frightened away?
34 On what was the giant bird called the Roc in the story of Sinbad the Sailor probably based?

Answers

1 By driving a red-hot stake into his eye.
2 Its tail.
3 It means "terrible lizard."
4 By rewinding the ball of thread he had tied to the entrance.
5 Fifteen centimetres.
6 At Cuckfield, Sussex, in 1822.
7 For picking its teeth and pushing itself off the ground after resting.
8 Brachiosaurus, which weighed 100 tonnes.
9 In Indonesia.
10 The wife of King Minos of Crete.
11 Because the pieces grew together.
12 They were 33cm long and 20cm wide.
13 Captain Seabury.
14 Because it was a symbol of war.
15 Seventy million years.
16 To help it cool down quickly.
17 Sandstorms.
18 The Geats.
19 With their rhythmic songs.
20 Six metres.
21 In 1924.
22 More than two thirds. To be exact, 70.8 percent.
23 750 AD.

24 The weather, particularly the rains.
25 By passing an electric current which helped crops to grow.
26 The Vickers Oceanics submarine, through its body.
27 In 1811.
"Pieces."
28 Ten.
29 In the Triassic, Jurassic and Cretaceous periods.
30 They turned to stone.
31 3,000.
32 Stories told by sailors.
33 By the smell of burning feathers.
34 The Apatornis.

How did you score?

34 correct. Excellent. Are you sure that you did not cheat?
25 or more. Good. Try to get a still better score in the Ghosts quiz.
15-25. Not so good. Check up the page and
questions that you got wrong. Try the quiz again in a few hours and see if you can do better.
Below 15, you had better read Monsters again!

ALL ABOUT GHOSTS

An American Indian legend tells of the flying head of a phantom warrior which had the wings of a bat and the claws of an eagle.

Phantom coaches often feature in ghost stories. Drivers and horses are almost always headless. The one shown here, spotted in the 1800's is an exception to the rule.

The most famous phantom ship is the Flying Dutchman, doomed to sail the seas forever. Sailors often claimed to have seen this ship when making the perilous journey around the Cape of Good Hope off South Africa. Sighting the Dutchman was supposed to be an omen of disaster.

▶ Ghosts are often claimed to be hallucinations. Certainly people can be tricked into 'seeing' things that do not exist. Stare at the cross in the centre of the skull, while you count slowly to 120. Then look at a plain wall. You should 'see' a phantom skull.

Written by
Christopher Maynard

Designed by
John Jamieson

Special consultant
Eric Maple

Illustrators
Roland Berry
Gordon Davies
John Francis
Brian Lewis
Malcolm McGregor
Michael Roffe

Special photography
John Jamieson
Christopher Maynard

Acknowledgements
We wish to thank the following individuals and organizations for their assistance and for making available information and photographs from their collections.
Harry Price library
RF Lord
Mary Evans Picture Library
National Laboratory of Psychical Research
Psychic News
Radio Times Hulton Picture Library
SPR (Society for Psychical Research)
Syndication International

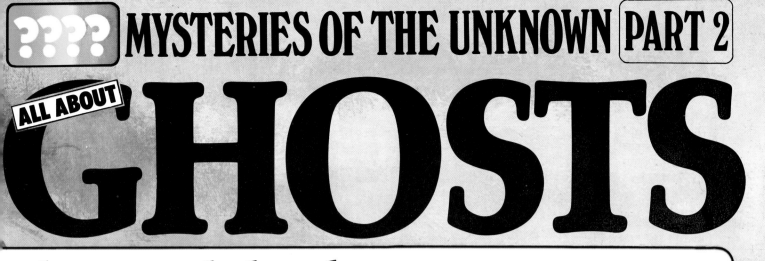
Ghosts and ghostlore

This part of the book is for those who shiver at shadowy forms in the dark, who hear strange noises in the night or who feel the presence of a 'something' from the unknown.

Ghost stories are as old as recorded history – perhaps even older – and they exist all over the world.

In the following pages you will meet haunting spirits, demon dogs, phantom ships, gallows ghosts, screaming skulls and many more.

You will also discover how professional ghost hunters, called psychic researchers, track down ghosts with special techniques and equipment. Many 'ghosts' are not ghosts at all – you will find out some of the odd things which people have mistaken for beings from beyond the grave.

You can also read about some of the recent theories which attempt to explain the possible existence of ghosts.

What is a ghost?

Ghosts are supposed to be the appearances of the spirits of the dead in a form visible to the living.

According to those who have claimed to see ghosts, they usually look pale and cloudy. They can pass through solid objects such as doors and walls. They appear and vanish leaving no trace.

Whether they really do exist is still a complete mystery, but perhaps this book will help you to make up your mind.

The story told below has many features associated with the creation of a ghost.

Tom Colley's ghost

In 1751, near the town of Tring in England, an old couple were beaten and drowned by a frenzied mob who thought they were witches. The leader of the mob, Tom Colley, was later arrested and sentenced to death by hanging. When he was dead, his body was suspended from the gallows (like that shown on the right) inside a gibbet – a cage of iron hoops and chains. It was left to dangle there as a gruesome warning to other lawbreakers.

People believed that a person's spirit could not leave the Earth to go to the afterlife – heaven or hell – without a burial ceremony. So Colley's ghost would haunt the spot where he was left to rot. Other ghosts were thought to be the spirits of people who had been murdered or who had died very suddenly.

Warding off ghosts

Colley's body, in its gibbet, was suspended at a crossroads. It was thought that his ghost would be confused by all the roads. Therefore, it would not be able to find its way back to take revenge on the people who had hanged him there.

His ghost is still said to haunt the place of the hanging. Recent stories say that his ghost now appears as a large black dog.

Types of ghost

Haunting Ghosts

▲ Haunting ghosts are seen at different times and by different people yet it is always the same ghost that appears in the same place. They seem to be totally unaware of living people. They are only attracted by the place which they haunt. Animals as well as people can be ghosts.

Ghosts of the living

▲ Strangely enough, many ghosts that are reported are of living people. The witness will suddenly see the ghost of a friend or relative, who is near death or in great trouble. Yet the person whose ghost it is may be many miles away. Such ghosts usually appear only once.

Purposeful ghosts

▲ Sometimes ghosts appear for a special reason. These ghosts are the phantoms of dead people appearing to give warnings or messages to the living, usually to family or close friends. The ghost rarely speaks, but it points or makes signs to deliver its message.

Duties of a ghost

Many legends tell of ghosts that appear because they have special tasks to carry out.

💀 Some ghosts return to avenge a murder and to expose the guilty villain.

💀 Other ghosts have to set right an injustice from which someone is still suffering. They make sure that money or property is returned to its rightful owner.

💀 Ghosts also come back to put right any wrongs they may have committed when alive.

💀 Sometimes ghosts appear to reveal the hiding place in which they hoarded money or treasure.

Poltergeists

Poltergeist activity is responsible for some rather alarming aspects of the supernatural, such as these cups and saucers flying through the air. Many people think that poltergeists are ghosts, but they do not behave like 'normal' ghosts.

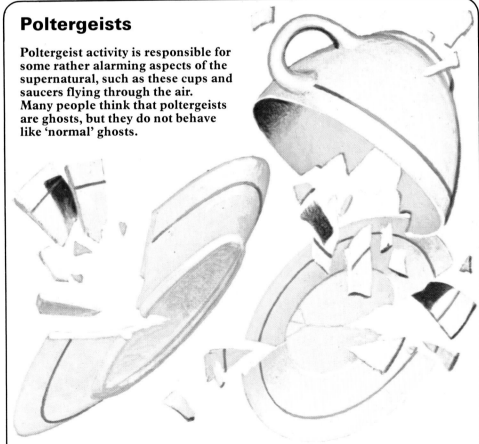

Objects being moved during poltergeist activity behave very oddly. They can be too hot to handle. They can move through doors or windows too small to let them through. And, most mysterious, they can suddenly appear in mid-air.

Poltergeist activity usually happens when people between the ages of 12 and 16 are present, although it is not known why. One theory supposes that their minds may generate the mysterious power needed. Researchers call this unknown power psychokinesis – PK – the ability to move objects without touching them. If they are correct and PK exists, then there are no ghosts involved, just the side-effects of PK energy.

Ghosts of long ago

The belief in ghosts is at least as old as recorded history. Stone Age people buried their dead in a way that suggests that they believed in ghosts: skeletons have been found that were weighed down with stones or bound hand and foot with cords. Perhaps this was to prevent the dead person's ghost from rising up and wandering.

The legends of the ancient Greeks and Romans are filled with phantoms of the dead. Greek ghosts seemed to interfere with the living more than ghosts in modern stories do. Most Greek ghosts were believed to be cruel, terrorizing people, causing trouble.

▲ The first record of a ghost comes from the Epic of Gilgamesh, an old Babylonian tale, written in 2,000 BC. The story is etched in clay tablets. It tells of the hero Gilgamesh and the ghost of his dead friend which appeared as a transparent shape.

▲ The ancient Egyptians believed that bird-headed ghosts, called khu, were spirits of the dead. These evil spectres were thought to spread disease among human beings and to be able to invade the bodies of animals, driving them into howling madness.

▲ Some Greek ghosts, like the one above, appeared in the form of evil, menacing phantoms. These smoky shapes were said to snort violently, breathing out black smoke and giving off a foul stench.

The haunted villa of Athens

Haunted houses are a common theme of many ghost stories. The earliest record of a haunted house is about 2,000 years old. The tale, described below, comes from ancient Greece.

At that time, a villa in Athens was said to be haunted. Every night a mournful spectre wandered through the villa, clanking and shaking the heavy prison manacles and iron chains that bound its hands and feet. The people who rented the villa were driven from it in terror, and one even died of fright.

House to rent – the ghost comes free

In desperation, the landlord of the villa was forced to lower the rent to next to nothing. The bargain price for which the house was being let came to the attention of a philosopher called Athenodorus. He looked at the house and was delighted to rent it for so little money, ghost or no ghost. Athenodorus was fascinated by the story of the haunting and wanted to discover what lay at the bottom of the mystery.

The ghost appears

The first evening after moving in, as Athenodorus sat quietly working, he was interrupted by the ominous sound of clattering chains. Acting as if nothing were wrong, he calmly carried on with his work. The noise grew louder. Then the grey-haired ghost of an old man came into the room, gesturing and signalling for Athenodorus to get up and follow. The philosopher continued to ignore the phantom. The ghost drew nearer until it was hovering right over him. Athenodorus still took no notice. Finally, the defeated spectre turned and went back the way it had come, vanishing at last in the courtyard. Athenodorus watched and saw exactly where it disappeared.

The ghost laid to rest

The next day he returned to the spot with a magistrate and some workmen who dug up the site. They unearthed a skeleton shackled to a mound of rusting chains. After the bones were buried in a cemetery, the haunting stopped. Neither the ghost nor its shackles were ever seen again.

▲ Roman history is full of ghost tales. In 44 BC Brutus, an army general, headed a plot to murder Julius Caesar. On March 15, he and his fellow conspirators stabbed Caesar to death. Not long afterwards Brutus was visited by a huge frightening phantom which claimed to be the ghost of his evil genius. When the spectre reappeared in Brutus' tent (shown above) the night before battle, its purpose became clear – the phantom was an omen of doom. Brutus lost the battle and killed himself afterwards.★

▲ Although the ancient Chinese had great respect for their dead ancestors and even held feasts in their honour, they were terrified of the spirits of murdered people which were considered to be evil. When a Chinese ghost like this appeared, it was thought to be dressed in the clothes it had worn when alive. Its arrival was impressive. First, it appeared as a shapeless cloud, out of which the head and feet emerged. Finally the body formed, surrounded by a glowing green cloud.

Spotting a ghost

There is no easy answer to the question 'What does a ghost look like?' Ghosts vary greatly in appearance; some are transparent shapes, some are dark shadowy figures, others look completely lifelike. But over the years, some general characteristics of ghosts have been noted which may help you to spot a ghost.

 A ghost often wears strange or old-fashioned clothes.

 A ghost almost never speaks, even if it is spoken to.

 A ghost may vanish into thin air, walk through a wall or through the air.

 A ghost may suddenly materialize in a locked room, so making an 'impossible' appearance.

| ???? | ★ In Shakespeare's play, the phantom is described as being that of Julius Caesar. |

Strange customs

Ghosts usually inspire fear when they appear. Many people believe that ghosts are evil creatures which will harm living people.

In the past people invented all kinds of strange customs to protect themselves from ghosts. Many of these practices depended on the belief that ghosts still behaved in the same way that they had done during their life on Earth.

So people tried to frighten them with loud noises and fire, to outwit them with clever tricks or to chase them away with strange rituals.

Keeping lemures at bay

The Romans were careful to avoid lemures, supposedly the ghosts of people who had led evil lives. Special festivals were held every year in May to keep away the lemures. Even today it is considered bad luck to be married during that month.

Frightened of noise

During these celebrations, drums were pounded. The ghosts were supposed to be afraid of the noise and the din was thought to make them fly away in fright. Just to be sure, black beans, shown in the picture above, were also burnt by the side of graves. The Romans believed that the foul-smelling smoke of the beans would be certain to keep lemures away.

Outwitting a rhea's ghost

Rheas are big flightless birds, similar to ostriches, that live in South America. The Lengua indians of South America used to hunt rheas. But having killed a bird, the indians thought that the rhea's ghost would try to reclaim its body. To prevent this, the indians used a trick to outwit the rhea's ghost. They plucked the feathers from the dead body's chest, leaving them in piles along the way home. Whenever the pursuing ghost came across the feathers, it stopped to see whether the pile was its whole body or only a part. Thus, the hunters had time to hurry home safely. The ghost was too timid to enter their village.

Nailing down the afrit

▲ The Arabs of the Middle East lived in great fear of evil spirits. They were especially frightened of being haunted by the spirits of people who had been murdered. They believed that a phantom, called an afrit, would rise from the spot where the murdered person's blood had splashed to the ground. There was only one way to stop this happening. A new nail had to be hammered into the earth exactly on the spot where the killing had taken place. The picture above shows the bloodstain being nailed firmly to the ground.

Befriending the ghost of a bear

▲ A bear hunt was an important event for the Indian tribes of North America. Before setting out, they held long fasts and made sacrifices to the ghosts of bears that had been killed in former hunts. This was to make the hunt a success. When a bear was killed it was brought back to the village and treated as an honoured guest. A chief's bonnet was placed on its head and bowls of food were set before it. Then it was politely invited to eat. Only after this elaborate ceremony to appease the dead animal's ghost was the bear skinned and cooked.

Flogging the graveyard ghost

▲ In the 17th century, witch hunts were common, and the supernatural was firmly believed in by people of every country. In south west England, a Reverend Dodge made a great name for himself as a fierce ghost-hunter. He would run along roads with a whip, shouting and flogging unseen spirits. He also lurked in churchyards, waiting to trap unwary ghosts. Whether he actually saw any is unproved, but according to one story, a ghost that he came across was so frightened that it gave out a loud cry and vanished forever.

HAUNTED PLACES
Where ghosts gather

Ghosts are supposed to haunt the scene of death. It is therefore not surprising that many ghosts are reported at sites where death or violence on a large scale once took place.

You might expect the scene of a crash to be haunted by the same number of ghosts as those who died in it. But this is not always the case. It seems that for some unknown reason, only certain victims become ghosts.

Not everyone can see a ghost. Those who are able to do so are described as having psychic powers.

Ghosts on battlefields

An obvious place for a haunting ought to be a battlefield and a number of them are thought to harbour ghosts. Those that do so include Marathon in Greece, Waterloo in Belgium and Dunkirk in France.

Civil War phantoms

Shiloh in Tennessee, USA, is claimed to be haunted to this day. The Battle of Shiloh was a major conflict of the American Civil War. Two days of savage fighting in April, 1862 resulted in the deaths of over 24,000 men.

In the months that followed, stories of a phantom battle began to be told. The reports claimed that gunfire, the clashing of sabres and bayonets and the screams and shouts of dying men could be heard at the site of the battle. The picture on the right shows an impression of the phantom battle in action.

▲ Traditionally, the elm was a good tree from which to hang criminals. Its strong lower branches were ideal for suspending a noose. Elms are sometimes reputed to be haunted by the ghosts of the people who met an untimely end under their branches.

▲ A graveyard seems the natural place to find lots of ghosts. But this is not the case, as people rarely die in the graveyard itself. Ghosts normally haunt the place of death. Just one ghost is thought to exist in a graveyard. It is the 'graveyard guardian', the spirit of the first person to have been buried there. The guardian's task is to keep away evil spirits and unwanted intruders. An ancient ritual in Western Europe was to sacrifice a living person when a new burial ground was established, to make sure that it would have its guardian.

A special burial place

Until the late 19th century, the north side of a church graveyard (shown in black on the plan view below), was rarely used to bury people in. It was the part of the churchyard often cast in gloom and shadow.

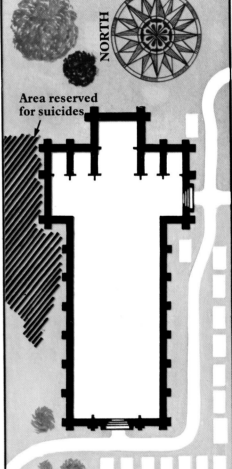

NORTH

Area reserved for suicides

The custom came from old Germanic beliefs. The area was suitable only for the restless souls (and possibly restless ghosts) of those who had committed suicide, which was considered an unpardonable sin. Suicides were also buried at crossroads. A stake was driven through their hearts, to stop a ghost from appearing at the spot. Even if it did, like Tom Colley's ghost, it would be confused by the four roads and stay in the same place until it faded away.

▲ There are many cases of people seeing and hearing the spirits of disaster victims, both before and after the event. The flaming crash of the R101 airship (shown above), was relived by a woman medium who was 'contacted' by the airship's captain. The airship had crashed in France two days earlier. The captain's voice, speaking through the medium, described the last moments of the flight. Its description proved to be accurate, as an official enquiry later showed. Perhaps this is a true contact from beyond the grave.

Phantoms of the sea

In the days of sailing ships, crews were often out of sight of land for weeks on end. Alone at sea, sailors had to face the perils of uncharted islands and reefs, sudden storms and freak giant waves. Sometimes ships disappeared and were never seen again. It is no wonder that sailors became famous for their superstitions and ghost stories.

Over the years, scores of phantom ships have been reported, gliding mysteriously across the waves. Ships that had ghosts as 'passengers' were thought to be jinxed – to have bad luck. A jinxed ship was doomed to encounter terrible disaster.

Captain Kidd's ghost

In 1701, the famous pirate leader Captain Kidd was captured and sentenced to death. He was hanged, then his dead body, shown on the right, was put in a gibbet as a warning to other pirates.

Like most pirate leaders, Captain Kidd buried his gold treasure. Then he killed the men who helped him bury it and left their ghosts to guard it. Years later, treasure hunters, digging for the loot, struck an iron chest. The chest instantly sank out of sight. A pirate ghost was supposed to have jumped out of the hole and attacked the men, driving them away in shrieking terror.

The unluckiest ship afloat

In 1858, the *Great Eastern* was the largest passenger ship in the world. Yet from the start, it was thought that the ship was jinxed. Several people were killed while building it and one workman, a riveter, vanished mysteriously as he hammered away in the hull. The ship's launching was a bad omen too. The ship stuck fast on the slip, and it was months before it floated free.

Launched at last

Only a few hours after steaming out to sea, one of the funnels blew up, killing six of the crew. During the first crossing the passengers were disturbed by the dull thuds of hammering from below. Then came a a terrible storm, during which the giant paddle wheels were ripped away from the sides of the ship. The crew panicked and refused to obey the captain's orders. The *Great Eastern* survived, but it never worked as a liner again, being used for laying telegraph cables. In 1885, the ship was towed to a breaker's yard. As the workers tore into the hull, they found the remains of the riveter who had been sealed in alive nearly 30 years before. Could it have been the sound of his ghostly hammering that had echoed throughout the ship's career?

▶ The *Great Eastern* had a double hull with one metre gap between the two sections. This was where the skeleton of the missing riveter and his bag of rusty tools were found.

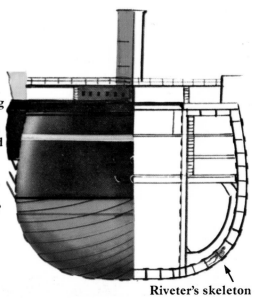

Riveter's skeleton

The haunted submarine

Many ghost stories have their origins in the strange events that occur during wartime. One of the most bizarre is about the haunted German submarine, the UB-65.

The UB-65 was built in 1916 during World War 1. During its construction, a series of accidents killed five men and injured several others. Although the submarine crew was highly superstitious and reluctant to sail, the ship was needed badly, and so it was launched despite the ominous signs of impending doom.

A near disaster

During the preparations for the submarine's first dive, a sailor threw himself over the side without warning. The captain continued the mission as if nothing had happened. But when he tried to surface, the UB-65 would not rise. Sea water began seeping into the ship, soon reaching the batteries and causing them to give off deadly fumes. At last, the desperate captain managed to surface with his crew almost dead from suffocation.

The phantom lieutenant

Back in port, the UB-65 was loading supplies when a torpedo exploded, killing six men including a lieutenant. Shortly after, a terrified petty officer and another sailor claimed the ghost of the dead lieutenant had come aboard. A few weeks later, while patrolling off the English coast, the ghost was spotted standing in the bows. The phantom appeared once more as the ship put into port. A few moments later the captain was killed as enemy planes attacked the harbour.

A chaplain was summoned to drive away, or exorcise, the ghost. For the next few months, the UB-65 functioned normally. Then suddenly the chief gunner went mad and killed himself, and the day after that, the petty officer jumped over the side. In the next battle the ship was hit. The lights inside the submarine flashed wildly, and an eerie green glow filled the hull. Once more the damaged UB-65 limped back to port.

The final sighting

Late in the war, an American ship came across a strange sight. The crew saw the UB-65 abandoned and drifting at sea. Suddenly an explosion tore through the submarine. Before it slid under, the figure of the ghostly officer appeared for the last time.

Unlikely ghosts

Ghosts are normally phantoms of either living or dead people. But ghosts of animals and even of objects have been seen. There are countless tales of phantom fire-breathing horses galloping through the night.

Ghosts do not have to be of living things. Tales of phantom ships have been told for centuries, and today there are stories of ghostly cars, buses and aeroplanes.

In the future, there will probably be stories of phantom spaceships, astronauts, and perhaps of strange creatures on other worlds.

▲ The phantom machine shown above is the ghost of a Spitfire fighter plane. The howling sound of its engine is said to be heard as it flies a low victory roll over its former airfield, the World War 2 airbase of Biggin Hill, England.

1 The talking mongoose

One of the most bizarre hauntings on record is that of a talking mongoose named Gef. Haunting ghosts almost never speak to people. Certainly animal ghosts are not supposed to – yet Gef the mongoose not only spoke but also told jokes and stories, swore and sang songs.

Nobody could make out just what Gef actually was. He was not a poltergeist at work; nor did he seem to be an hallucination or a hoax. He simply claimed that he was a ghost in the form of a small mongoose.

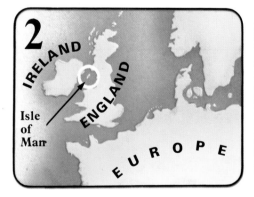

2

▲ The Isle of Man lies between Ireland and England. It is supposedly a centre of witchcraft, and it is also said to be heavily haunted. In the 1930s, a mysterious talking mongoose appeared on the island near its west coast town of Dalby.

3

▲ The talking mongoose, who said his name was Gef, haunted an old seaside farmhouse. The first signs of him appeared when the owners began to see a shadow prowling about the house nibbling food, rattling saucers and, for some reason, blowing out candles.

The phantom hound

For centuries, huge phantom dogs have cropped up in ghost legends. They are known all over northern Europe and in parts of North America.

At night demon dogs haunted lonely country roads, graveyards and old gallows sites. According to legend, anyone who saw a phantom hound would soon be stricken with disaster or death. Luckily, these dogs left people alone unless provoked.

Black Shuck

One of the dogs, shown here, was known as Black Shuck. It was supposed to be an enormous beast, the size of a calf. Its shaggy coat was as black as soot. One of the things that made Black Shuck different from other ghostly dogs was its eye. This was a single cyclops-eye, as large as a saucer, in the centre of its forehead. The dog had a fiendish howl. Foam and fire dripped from its jaws and its breath blew like a strong gust of wind.

The ghostly lift

In 1969, a large rambling seaside hotel in Wales was awaiting demolition. But before the demolition crew could arrive, a number of strange things took place as if the old hotel were protesting against its undignified end.

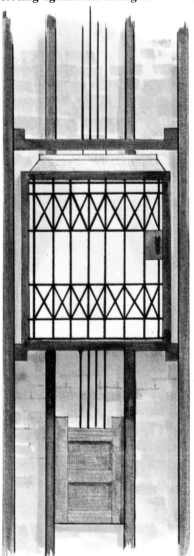

The main mystery was the lift that began to move by itself. Without warning, it would rise from the ground floor to the second floor and stop. This should have been impossible as the electricity had been switched off weeks before. Eventually, the lift's cables were cut, but even that did not stop it. Workmen had to climb into the shaft and pound the lift with sledge hammers before it finally crashed to the bottom of its shaft.

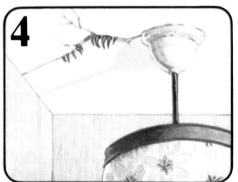

▲ One day, the owner of the house saw a pair of furry paws poke out from a crack in the ceiling. She tried to touch them but instead was bitten. Then a high shrill voice, speaking in excellent English, told her to go and put ointment on the bite.

▲ Gef became famous and was featured in many newspaper stories. But he has not made an appearance for many years. The farmhouse was sold and the new owners reported having shot a strange little animal in the grounds. Could this have been Gef?

The haunted house

Many ghosts haunt one particular place such as the house where they once lived. These haunting spirits are seen time and time again, wandering through the house.

Haunting ghosts are thought to occur because of a violent or dramatic event in the past which links a spirit to a place. Houses where a brutal crime was committed or someone was bitterly unhappy are often haunted.

Some of the strange noises which make people think a house is haunted are caused by natural events, such as the creaking of shrinking and expanding timbers or the sound of rats and mice scurrying about.

Inside the house

Many strange things can occur in a haunted house. Here are some of them. The numbers below link with the numbers on the picture.

1   A ghostly figure glides from room to room passing straight through solid walls.

2   The curtains in a closed room start swaying in a mysterious breeze.

3   A skeleton is found walled up inside a hidden secret room.

4   The ghost of a member of the family materializes in front of its own, suddenly blank portrait.

5   Muddy footprints appear on the stairway as the thud of slow heavy footsteps is heard.

6   In the attic, objects move and fall to the floor while strange thumpings and bangings are heard.

7   An old skull screams whenever it is moved from the house to be buried.

8   A grandfather clock chimes thirteen, foretelling a death in the family.

9   A bloodstain on the floor cannot be removed. No matter how many times it is washed away, it always returns.

10   Groaning sounds come from a secret, cobweb-choked passage which leads from the fireplace to an upstairs room.

11   A pair of white-gloved hands appears at the piano and begins to play a funeral march.

12   Unseen forces set a chandelier swaying so violently that pieces of crystal crash to the floor.

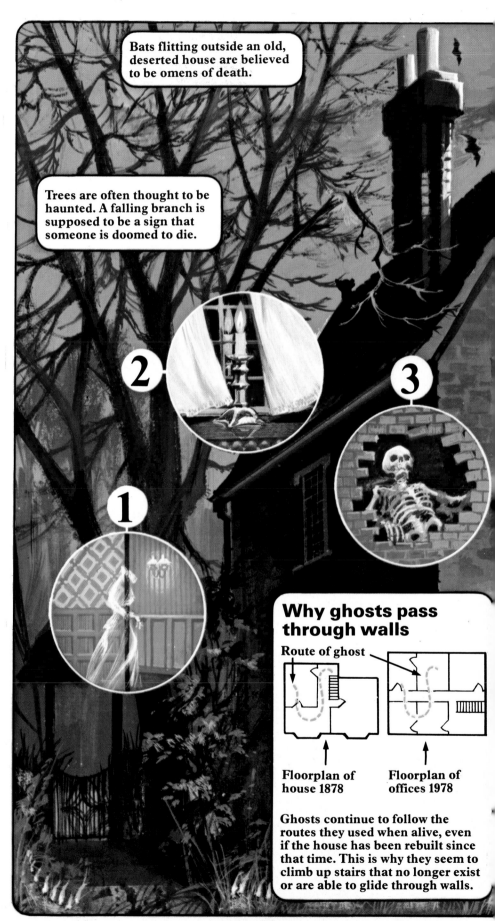

Bats flitting outside an old, deserted house are believed to be omens of death.

Trees are often thought to be haunted. A falling branch is supposed to be a sign that someone is doomed to die.

Why ghosts pass through walls

Route of ghost

Floorplan of house 1878

Floorplan of offices 1978

Ghosts continue to follow the routes they used when alive, even if the house has been rebuilt since that time. This is why they seem to climb up stairs that no longer exist or are able to glide through walls.

The sudden hoot of an owl is a warning that death is about to strike.

Corpse lights are small flames flickering just above the ground. Especially common in graveyards, they are said to show the way that a funeral procession will soon pass.

HAUNTED PLACES
The village with a dozen ghosts

Some places have a reputation for being particularly haunted. The village of Pluckley in south-east England is one of these. It is claimed to have no fewer than 12 ghosts.

The villagers do not agree as to whether the ghosts exist, but it seems unlikely that the village should get its reputation for no reason at all.

Researchers point out that conflicting opinions about ghosts can be a sign that they really do exist. If everyone had the same opinion, it would probably mean that they had read the same book or newspaper report.

The photographs on this page were taken recently. There were no signs of supernatural activity when the photographer took the pictures, and as you can see, no phantoms appeared on them.

The colonel of the woods

Park Wood was formerly a small stretch of forested ground on the outskirts of Pluckley. In recent times, it was cleared to become grazing land as you can see from the picture above. A colonel once hanged himself in the woods and his ghost used to be seen walking in them.

The hanging body of the schoolmaster

Soon after World War 1, a schoolmaster committed suicide in the village. He hanged himself from a laurel tree that stood in the road once known as Dicky Buss's Lane. His phantom body is said to be visible to this day, swinging in the breeze.

The spectre of the highwayman

The ghost of a highwayman haunts the area where a hollow oak tree stood at Fright Corner. Here the man was ambushed by his enemies. He was run through with a sword and speared to the tree. The gory event is said to be re-enacted every night.

The Pinnock

Fright Corner

A phantom coach and horses

The road from Pluckley to nearby Maltman's Hill is haunted by a phantom coach drawn by four horses. On dark nights it is supposed to be possible to hear the drumming of horses' hooves and the sound of the coach rumbling along the lonely road.

The ghost of the gypsy woman

The spectre of a pipe-smoking gypsy woman, huddled in a tattered shawl, is often claimed to be visible near the bridge by the crossroads. She was burned to death in mysterious circumstances and has haunted the site ever since.

The black ghost of the miller

Near a house called The Pinnock is an old ruined mill where the black shape of a miller's ghost is said to wander. The ghost only appears before a thunderstorm breaks over the village.

Pluckley railway station

Clay-pit and brickworks

50

The Red Lady and a mysterious modern ghost

The Church of St Nicholas, left, is said to be haunted by the ghost of the beautiful Lady Dering who died in the 12th century. She was buried in a sumptuous gown with a red rose in her hands. Her body was placed inside seven lead coffins, one inside the other, which were then put into an oak casket that was buried in a vault under the church. To this day her ghost, known as the Red Lady, walks in the graveyard of the church. Recently, there have also been reports of another mysterious female figure wandering inside the church, above right. She may be Pluckley's newest ghost.

NORTH

PLUCKLEY

Park Wood

Dicky Buss's Lane

Church of St Nicholas

Greystones

Rose Court

Surrenden Dering

The White Lady of Dering

Surrenden Dering was the manor of the Dering family. The main house was burnt by a fire in 1952. The house was supposed to have been haunted for centuries by the ghost of another member of the family, known as the White Lady, who appeared gliding through the library.

The ghost of the screaming man

Near the railway station is a clay-pit and a brickworks. A worker was smothered to death when a wall of clay fell on him. His ghost, which is said to haunt the site, screams in the same way as he did when he died.

The Lady of Rose Court

The house known as Rose Court is supposed to be haunted by the spirit of a former owner. She killed herself by drinking the juices of crushed poisonous berries. Her ghost appears between four and five o'clock in the afternoon, the time of day when she died.

The phantom monk

At a house called Greystones, a phantom monk is said to haunt the grounds. He is often seen with the lady of Rose Court. There seems to have been a mysterious connection between the two of them for she died by a window, looking towards Greystones.

0   500 metres

Scale of map

Ghosts around the world

Ghost stories and legends occur in countries all over the world.

The spirits come in all shapes and sizes. They behave in many different ways, mainly based on the customs of the area which they are thought to haunt.

Many of the ghosts are created by people's imagination. But one question remains unanswered – if ghosts do not exist, why should so many stories have been invented about them?

These pages show you just a few of the phantoms which, perhaps, haunt the Earth.

The railway ghost

There is an American legend that claims that the ghostly funeral train shown here of President Abraham Lincoln still rumbles along the railway track in New York State, more than 100 years after his death.

The glowing ghost

This ghostly apparition seemed to foretell the death of Roderigo Borgia in 15th century Italy. Minutes after the glowing ghost was seen, Borgia fell screaming to the ground, dying from the poisoned wine that he had drunk.

To Mexico

The bandit ghost

In Mexico, ghosts of people who had died violently were said to be able to cure illness. The ghost of the famous bandit, Pancho Villa, cured an insane boy by whipping and shouting to drive out the evil spirits thought to possess him.

The slave ghost

In southern Africa, people believed that if a witch doctor dug up a corpse and stole part of the body, he could turn its ghost into a slave. Then the witch doctor sent the ghost out to do his evil deeds – to spread sickness and kill his enemies.

The legless ghost

Japanese ghosts were believed to be deformed as a punishment for evil deeds when alive. Many were legless, their lower limbs engulfed in flames. According to legend, they warned people when death was near.

The eating ghost

The people of the Banks Islands in the Pacific Ocean believed that certain stones were haunted by 'eating ghosts'. If a person's shadow fell across such a stone the ghost was thought to suck out the person's soul. After losing his soul, the person died. These stones were placed in empty houses to keep away thieves.

PACIFIC OCEAN

A S I A

INDIA

AUSTRALIA

The gibbering ghost

The waterfall ghost

Indians believed in ghosts called bauta. They were hideous creatures with small, red bodies and huge, lion-like teeth. They gibbered through their noses when they spoke. They were supposed to roam at night, attacking people.

In 1905, two men on holiday saw a pair of ghostly hands come out of a waterfall. The hands beckoned to them. Looking behind the waterfall, they found a cave with three skeletons in it. The ghostly presence had fulfilled its task – to draw attention to the remains of of the dead.

Ghost hunting

Many people claim to have seen ghosts, but very few can offer any kind of proof.

Professional ghost hunters, called psychic researchers, are brought in to examine places which are thought to be haunted.

Although the investigators may have lots of scientific equipment to study any supernatural happenings, investigating ghosts is not easy.

Usually the investigators work with second-hand evidence and reports from witnesses. They must also try to discover whether the 'ghost' is a fake or whether it was caused by some natural event.

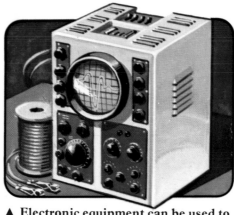

▲ Electronic equipment can be used to measure temperature and humidity and to detect the draughts and vibrations associated with ghosts. However, some investigators claim that their electronic gear (shown above) can even detect the 'psychic energy' of ghosts.

▲ A thin layer of flour or powder brushed on floors, ledges and stairways will show up any footprints or fingerprints made by fake 'ghosts'. Flour can also be dusted around furniture and other objects to reveal whether they have been moved.

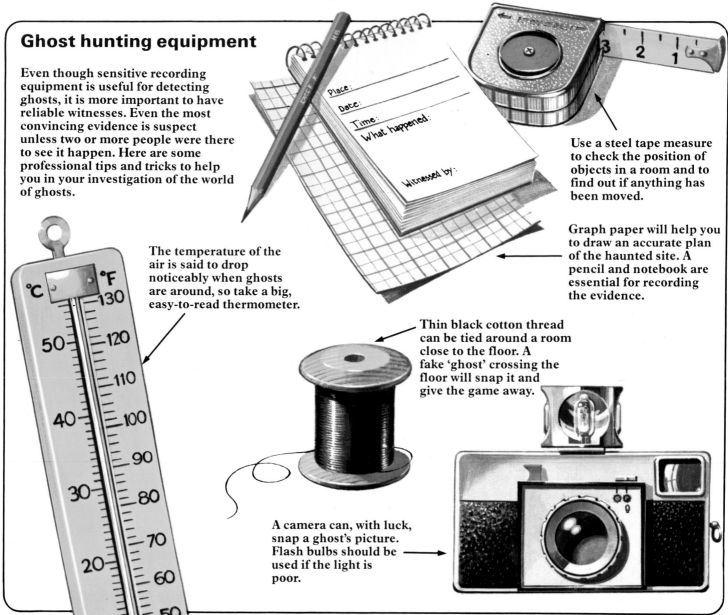

Ghost hunting equipment

Even though sensitive recording equipment is useful for detecting ghosts, it is more important to have reliable witnesses. Even the most convincing evidence is suspect unless two or more people were there to see it happen. Here are some professional tips and tricks to help you in your investigation of the world of ghosts.

Use a steel tape measure to check the position of objects in a room and to find out if anything has been moved.

Graph paper will help you to draw an accurate plan of the haunted site. A pencil and notebook are essential for recording the evidence.

The temperature of the air is said to drop noticeably when ghosts are around, so take a big, easy-to-read thermometer.

Thin black cotton thread can be tied around a room close to the floor. A fake 'ghost' crossing the floor will snap it and give the game away.

A camera can, with luck, snap a ghost's picture. Flash bulbs should be used if the light is poor.

Professional ghost hunting

A psychic researcher was called in to investigate a house where three people had reported strange events which made them believe the house was haunted.

The researcher arranged to spend the night in the room in which the ghost had appeared. He took with him a trunk of equipment to detect and record everything that happened.

Setting up the equipment

On arrival, the first thing the researcher did was to question the occupants about what they had seen and heard. Then he prepared the room for the night.

First the door and window were sealed shut with tape. A length of thread was placed all around the room so that anything brushing against it would set off a camera loaded with infra-red film, which could take photographs in the dark.

The researcher also put into position a draught-measuring device and a heat-sensitive switch which would set off the camera if the temperature changed. Beside the bed he placed a normal flash-equipped camera and a tape recorder.

Lastly, he ran a hearing aid from the infra-red camera to the bed so that he could hear it click from where he slept. A recording thermometer and a barometer were also set working.

The end of the investigation

The night passed quietly. Even with the carefully prepared traps, however, there was not the slightest sign of a ghost. Once again, a phantom had refused to co-operate.

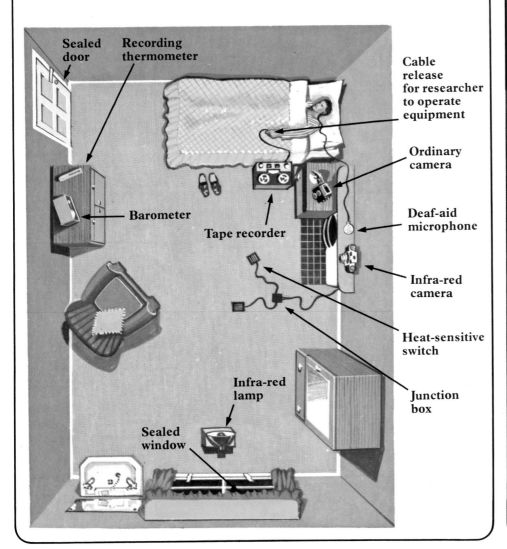

Sealed door

Recording thermometer

Barometer

Tape recorder

Cable release for researcher to operate equipment

Ordinary camera

Deaf-aid microphone

Infra-red camera

Heat-sensitive switch

Junction box

Infra-red lamp

Sealed window

Animal investigators

Some animals are known to be more aware of ghosts than people. They can be curiously sensitive to the strange stmosphere that lingers in haunted places. For this reason, investigators sometimes use animals to look for ghosts.

An American ghost hunter, investigating a house in Kentucky that was supposed to have a haunted room, took with him a rat, a cat, a dog and a rattlesnake. The animals were put into the haunted room one at a time.

The rat behaved normally, but the other animals all reacted in a surprising way. The rattlesnake at once reared up to strike an empty chair in the room. When the cat was carried into the room, it leapt to the floor and hissed and glowered at the same empty chair. The dog ran from the room snarling. It refused to go back.

Later, when the animals were tested in another room, they all behaved normally. The ghost hunter concluded that the animals could sense a ghostly presence in the haunted room which could not be sensed by human beings.

Ghost stories explained

Many ghost stories turn out to be untrue once psychic researchers look into them. Often they find that the signs which people took to be a ghost have a perfectly ordinary explanation.

It is not hard to understand why peoples in the past believed in ghosts as there was little scientific knowledge of how natural events were caused.

Today, investigators often find that people are actually disappointed rather than pleased when they are told that a 'ghost' was just the wind or flowing water. It seems that people would prefer to believe in ghosts.

Knockings at Netherfield

In 1946, a front page story in a newspaper caught the attention of two psychic researchers. The story was about a house that was filled with strange noises. It was thought that the house was haunted.

When the researchers arrived on the scene, they were told that hollow knocking sounds had been heard coming from the kitchen ceiling for several years. The researchers decided to spend the night in the house but first they checked the bedroom above for possible natural causes. Finding an alarm clock on a bedside chair, they took it downstairs with them.

That night faint knocking sounds came from the kitchen itself. The investigators traced the sound to the clock. Taking it apart, they found that the tightly wound spring was unwinding in jerks and making the faintest of tapping sounds.

The ghost revealed

The tapping noise itself was barely noticeable. But when the clock stood upstairs on the bedside chair, the noises it made passed down the chair legs, through the floor and were amplified to a loud knocking by the very thin plaster of the kitchen ceiling. So the 'ghost' was an alarm clock.

1 Ghosts from under the ground

This true story shows how unseen events can convince even the most sceptical people that ghosts are present.

The rumblings and noises that shook the house were investigated by lots of people, yet they did not find what was causing the 'haunting'. Although, as you will see, the cause proved to be a natural one, it is not surprising that it remained hidden until psychic researchers conducted a thorough investigation.

▲ In the 1950s, a house in Yorkshire, England, was invaded by mysterious eerie noises. Explosions and the sounds of banging, as if doors were being slammed, continued over a period of some months. The loudest noises literally shook the walls of the house.

▲ The two doctors who used the house as a surgery called in a plumber to inspect the water pipes. They also had the gas and electrical systems examined. Even the police came to inspect the house. But no-one could find a reason for the noises.

▲ The research team went outside to examine the foundations of the house. They found an old sewer, no longer used, in the garden, where earlier the ground had sunk but had since been filled in. The sewer passed very near the house, but it was choked with dirt and earth.

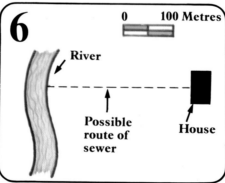

▲ They could not crawl along the sewer, but its direction showed that it emptied into a nearby river. The river was tidal – its level went up and down depending on the sea. The researchers hunted for the sewer's outlet along the banks of the river but without success.

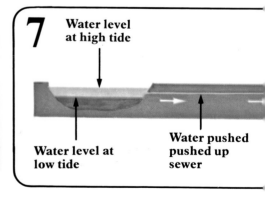

▲ The diagram above shows a cross-section through the soil between the house and the river. The researchers found that high tides were forcing water up the sewer, and despite its semi-blocked state, water was seeping through the soil under the house. The

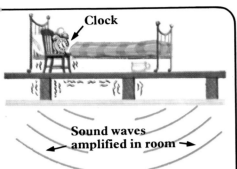

Clock

Sound waves
amplified in room

▲ This diagram shows how the clock spring's tapping turned into a ghostly knocking. The vibration passed down the legs of the bedside chair, then through the floor and the joists. The thin plaster ceiling amplified the vibrations into the room below.

4

▲ The doctors, wondering if the house were haunted, asked a team of psychic researchers to investigate. The team noticed cracks in the walls, badly fitting doors and a dip in the roof. These all seemed to be signs that the house was moving on its foundations.

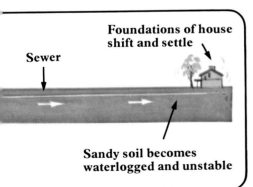

Foundations of house shift and settle

Sewer

Sandy soil becomes waterlogged and unstable

foundations of the house were settling, and the movements were causing the noises that had been heard. The final proof was that the noises were loudest when the tide was at its highest. So the psychic researchers recorded it as yet another 'haunting' with a natural cause.

Spectres of the Brocken

For centuries people have reported seeing huge ghostly figures haunting the Harz mountains in West Germany. It was believed that these ghosts gathered together once a year in May on the summit of the Brocken, the highest mountain in the region.

However, less than a century ago this ghost legend was shown to have a natural explanation. It was people's imaginations that had turned it into a ghost story.

It turned out that the phantoms of the Brocken were nothing more than the shadows of climbers that had been cast onto clouds swirling around the peak. The climbers had to be on or near the summit, and the weather conditions had to be just right for the 'ghosts' to appear.

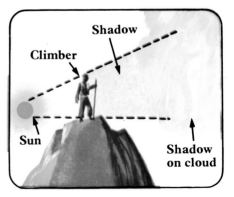

Shadow

Climber

Sun

Shadow on cloud

▲ Ghostly figures were seen around the Brocken when the sun was setting and a bank of light cloud hung around the summit. Climbers' shadows projected onto the clouds could be as much as 200 metres high.

Clever fakes

Some ghosts cannot be explained by natural physical causes, or even by supernatural ones. When they are investigated they are found to be the work of human beings. In other words, they are fakes.

Convincing people that a fake ghost is real is not very hard. Most people are quite willing to accept that mysterious forces exist which cannot be explained.

Fake ghosts have been used to play upon people's natural fears and suspicions for all kinds of reasons. They have been invented to keep secrets hidden, to cover up murders and to cheat people out of their money.

▲ Smugglers, a few hundred years ago, were well known for using ghost legends to their own advantage when they made their illegal runs.

One smuggler cleverly gave new life to an old tale about a ghost carriage and a headless horse. He painted his horse white, except for its head. On the carriage which he used to carry his smuggled goods, the smuggler hung a set of lights. Anyone who met him at night would swear to having seen a headless horse pulling a glowing phantom carriage.

Ghost-faking equipment

Just a few of the gadgets used to 'contact' ghosts are shown here. Most attempts to contact the world of the dead were made in near-darkness, so it was easy to cheat. A simple gadget was the voice trumpet. It was used to 'throw' the medium's voice across the room, so that the hollow voice sounded like that of a ghost.

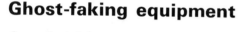

A rapping hand looked real enough in a darkened room. It could be made to move by squeezing a hidden tube of liquid-filled rubber. In the gloom of a seance, the 'living hand' would begin to tap out answers to the medium's questions.

Hidden tape recorders are perfect for making ghostly sounds. They can also be hooked to tiny microphones hidden in a medium's clothes and used to fool people into believing in 'voices of the dead.'

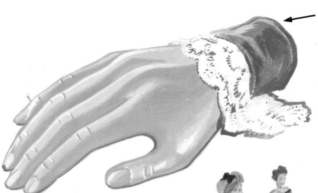

Trick slates were used to record the writing of spirits. The slates were prepared beforehand. A hidden spring would hide the blank slates then flip up already prepared ones with writing on them, supposedly messages from the dead.

Once people are convinced that a medium can contact ghosts, the rest is easy. All that is needed are proper tools and an eager audience. Most of the fake mediums who claimed they could reach the dead used tricks similar to the ones shown here. A 19th century drawing room scene like this was typical of a fake attempt to talk with the spirits of the dead.

Photographs of the dead

Spirit photographs were a tremendous craze in the late 19th century. Photography was then a new technology and most people believed that it was impossible to trick a camera. Photographers were flooded with requests to have pictures taken with ghosts of the dead.

Spirit photography became a great opportunity for frauds and cheats. By using photographic tricks and by tampering with film in the darkroom, spirit pictures were easy to make. Investigations revealed that in most cases the 'ghost' was a dummy, a

▲ The pictures in the left hand column above are examples of the sort of fake spirits that could be conjured up by a good photographer. In the right hand column is a sequence which has not been proved to be a fake. Taken in the 1930s, the pictures shown an Indian girl, Silver Belle, appearing in front of a medium. The audience of 81 people who watched the figure emerge found no evidence of cheating.

cardboard doll or a dressed-up assistant. So many photographs proved to be fakes that the public stopped believing in them altogether.

Sense or nonsense?

Many people are convinced that they have seen ghosts. But do ghosts really exist? Unfortunately the evidence gathered is not always reliable. Many accounts of ghosts are so far-fetched that they are obviously nonsense or outright fakes. Many other ghosts have been shown to be the result of odd light conditions playing tricks on the eyes.

There have been a number of attempts to explain ghosts. But the theories do not account for all aspects of ghostly behaviour. As the pictures opposite show, some evidence for ghosts is still unexplainable.

Who believes in ghosts?

People interviewed · People who had seen ghosts · Types of ghost seen

1,684 · 615 Living · 275 Dead · 639 Unknown · 155 Other

17,000

These ghosts were recognized by the people who saw them

One of the first tasks undertaken by researchers was to find out how many people claimed to have seen ghosts.

In 1890, they completed a survey which was carried out in several European countries. 17,000 people were questioned, and their answers are shown in the chart above. Studies which have been carried out since then have all shown similar results.

Two types of ghost

Modern theories of ghosts reject the idea that they are literally the 'spirits' of people.

Ghosts of the living are thought to be linked with telepathy. This is the name given to the mysterious (and unproven) ability of some people to send or receive messages without using physical methods. The brain is thought to interpret a telepathic signal as a visual image, or 'ghost'.

Ghosts of the dead are thought to be 'psychic images'. They were formed as the result of an extreme emotional event.

1 Ghosts of living people

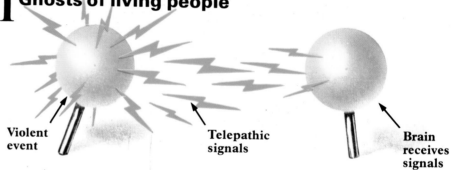

Violent event · Telepathic signals · Brain receives signals

It is thought that ghosts of living people could be formed like this.

Extreme danger or a crisis may cause the brain to send out telepathic thought signals, rather like a radio sending out an emergency SOS message. This signal can be received by the brain of a sensitive person, as the brain 'tunes in' to the SOS message. The brain interprets the signal as a picture, so it is thought to be a ghost.

2 Ghosts of the dead

A — Violent event · B — Psychic image formed · C — Image absorbs energy · D — Image remains for many years · E — Image fades away

Haunting ghosts (though not purposeful ghosts, which remain unexplained) are thought to be formed like this.

When a violent event occurs, such as a murder, an unknown force is generated to form a 'psychic image' at the spot where the death happened. The invisible image continues to exist by absorbing energy (such as heat) from the surrounding air. This could explain why the area of a haunting is usually cold.

The image survives for many years as a faithful record of the original event. It can be seen by people who are sensitive to the psychic forces which created it. Gradually however, it fades away, becoming fainter and fainter until it vanishes completely.

Mystery photographs

People believe photographs because cameras 'do not lie'. Yet the spirit pictures that were once all the rage were nearly all shown to be faked.

But photographs of ghosts that have not been tampered with at all are the hardest to understand. Although they are the best proof yet gathered that ghosts do exist, they raise more questions than they answer. If ghosts really are psychic images, then how can ordinary photographic film record them? Yet all three of these pictures are considered by experts to be genuine.

▲ The ghost of Raynham Hall was claimed to have the shape of a woman. In 1936 came startling proof. A photographer was setting up his equipment at the foot of the stairs. He saw a phantom drifting down them and hastily took the picture shown above.

▲ People commonly claim to see the ghosts of nuns and priests in churches. Often they are said to stand at or near the altar, praying. The photograph above of a cowled monk standing by an altar rail was taken in the early 1960s by the vicar of a church in England.

At the time he saw nothing that was out of the ordinary. But his developed film showed the tall phantom monk seen here. It appears to be about three metres tall. The film was carefully checked by photographic experts but showed no signs of tampering.

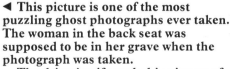

◀ This picture is one of the most puzzling ghost photographs ever taken. The woman in the back seat was supposed to be in her grave when the photograph was taken.

The driver's wife took this picture of her husband sitting in the car. She claims that there was nobody in the car except her husband. Yet the photograph clearly shows the figure of a woman – her mother – who had died a week before.

Experts say that the film has not been altered in any way. Yet if you look closely you will see that the corner of her scarf seems to overlap the side pillar of the car. This would only be possible if her face was placed in the picture after it was taken. Yet if the experts are correct and the photograph is genuine, there is no explanation for how it could have happened – unless the woman in the back was a ghost.

A dictionary of ghostlore

This dictionary of ghosts, ghostly events and related topics includes many of the subjects that have appeared in this book as well as some that are new. Together they make up only a very small part of the world of the unknown.

AFTERLIFE The place to which the human soul is believed to go after the body dies. Many people believe that a soul in the afterlife can contact the living, although it does not haunt the Earth.

APPARITION This is the term used by professional ghost researchers to describe all kinds of ghosts no matter whether they are human, animal or objects.

Artificial ghosts

Magicians of the Middle Ages tried all sorts of ways to contact the dead. Many French alchemists thought they could create ghosts out of human blood. They carried out experiments with heating samples of blood in charcoal burners like the one above. A number of doubtful reports claim that ghostly shapes really did appear in the clouds of steam.

Doppelganger

Also known as a fetch, this ghost is supposed to be the double of a living human being. If people are unfortunate enough to see their own doppelganger, it can be an omen that they will die in the near future.

ESP These initials stand for Extra Sensory Perception. Sight, sound, smell, touch, taste are the five known human senses. Other possible senses such as telepathy or psychokinesis are classed as ESP.

EXORCISM A ritual usually performed by a priest to drive out a spirit from the place it is haunting.

FADING GHOSTS A haunting ghost often fades away with time. But there are stories of ghosts of Roman legionaries which have been haunting for at least 1,600 years.

Fake ghosts

One of the cleverest tricks of the 19th century was to bring a phantom onto a stage. A large sheet of glass was angled in front of a ghost-playing actor who was hidden below the stage. The actor's brightly lit image was reflected onto the glass. But to the audience, the ghost seemed real, and the actors could pretend the ghost was with them on stage.

GHOST DANCE Ceremony performed by the Plains Indians of North America in the late 19th century. The dance was performed by Indians wearing 'ghost shirts'. The Indians thought that spirits would help them drive the white settlers from their territory.

GHOUL An especially nasty and evil-looking kind of spirit. Ghouls are supposed to feed on the dead.

CORPSE LIGHTS Flickering flames that are seen at times in graveyards. They are caused by gases seeping through the earth from corpses buried in shallow graves.

CROSSROADS GHOST Crossroads were a favourite place to hang criminals whose ghosts remain.

FOLKLORE The fairy tales, legends, beliefs and superstitions in which people over the ages have believed. Many are still believed in today.

GALLOWS GHOST This name is given to the ghost of a person who had been hanged for a crime. The ghost is said to hover near the place of death.

GRAVEYARD GUARDIAN The ghost of the first corpse to be buried in a cemetery. It protected the bodies buried in the graveyard from damage and evil spirits.

HALLUCINATION An image which seems real, even though it does not physically exist.

HAUNTING A situation in which a particular place is visited over and over again by the same ghost. Hauntings may happen anywhere from castles and houses, to shops, ships, motorways and airports. The cause of a haunting is usually some kind of tragic event, often a death, that occurred at the place where the ghost appears. The ghost is a kind of 'visible memory' of the event.

MARSHLIGHTS Shimmering, moving flames that are sometimes seen at night in marshes and other wet areas. They are also known as Will-o'-the wisps. Marshlights are caused when the gases of rotting vegetation begin to burn of their own accord. It was once said that they were the tiny ghosts of young children.

Noises of ghosts

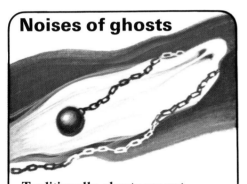

Traditionally, ghosts are not supposed to speak. But folklore is rarely consistent and some legends claimed that ghosts made feeble squeaking sounds like the chirping of birds. The Romans and Greeks believed that ghosts made strange gibbering and muttering sounds.

MEDIUM A person said to have psychic powers than enable him or her to contact the spirits of the dead and to receive their messages. A medium is often consulted by friends and relatives of the dead.

OPTICAL ILLUSION An instance in which people's eyes play tricks on them. What they see at that moment is not really there at all. An example of an optical illusion is the case of a ghostly car that was reported travelling the wrong way down a section of motorway. People imagined they saw the head-lights of another car coming towards them. In fact, a combination of motorway lights, car headlamps and mist had created an optical illusion.

PHANTOM Another term for a ghost. Yet another word for a ghost is spectre.

POLTERGEIST Thought to be a psychic disturbance, during which objects are launched through the air and a tremendous amount of noise is made. One explanation is that poltergeist activity is the result of psychokinesis. The word is German, meaning a noisy spirit.

PSYCHIC The word used to describe forces which have no physical explanation. It includes ESP, ghosts and other supernatural events.

PSYCHIC RESEARCH Investigations that are made by specially trained people trying to find the reasons behind reported ghost hauntings. Investigators sift through the evidence sorting the natural causes from the supernatural ones. The aim of all psychic research is to discover what the forces are which produce ghostly events.

PSYCHOKINESIS The ability to harness psychic forces and direct them at objects to make them move without touching them. Psychokinesis, or PK, is a completely unknown kind of force. Few of the people who have experienced it can control it at will.

SHADES OF THE DEAD A term to describe the dark, shadowy forms in which the spirits of the dead sometimes appear.

SHROUD The white flowing robe that a ghost is said to wear. In fact, shrouds were the sheets in which corpses were wrapped for burial. The ghosts that are most likely to wear them, therefore, are graveyard spirits. Most other ghosts however appear in normal, everyday clothes.

SOUL The spirit of a person. It is not part of the physical body and it cannot be touched or seen. It is believed to be immortal, surviving after the body dies. It used to be thought that a soul that could not pass into the afterlife remained to haunt the Earth as a ghost. One theory imagined that the shape of a soul in the afterlife was that of a butterfly emerging from its chrysalis.

Speaking to a ghost

In the 18th century it was said that a ghost could be commanded to speak if it were addressed firmly. It could be ordered to identify itself and declare its business among living people.

SPIRITUALISM A religious cult which believes among other things that the living can communicate with the spirits of the dead. This is done with a properly conducted ritual called a seance. The seance is led by a medium through whom the spirits can contact the living. Spiritualism began in America in 1848.

SUPERNATURAL Those events, and the forces that create them, which seem to defy the laws of nature and which are, at present, impossible for science to explain. Ghosts and spirits certainly fall into the realm of the supernatural as do telepathy, PK and other psychic forces.

SUPERSTITION A not always rational belief that certain objects and actions have supernatural meanings and in some way can bring about unlikely events, or good or bad luck. One example of a superstitious belief is that if a coin is placed on a

tombstone and is danced around seven times, the ghost within can be enticed into revealing itself, reaching out to snatch the money.

TELEPATHY The mysterious ability to communicate thoughts from one person to another over any distance without using physical means.

63

Creepy quiz

Have you got shivers of fear running up and down your spine? See how much you know about the world beyond the grave in this creepy quiz.

1 Where did the R101 airship crash?
2 How many ghosts is the village of Pluckley said to have?
3 How tall could the spectres of the Brocken be?
4 What are corpse lights said to show?
5 When was the Epic of Gilgamesh written?
6 The Flying Dutchman was supposed to be an omen of disaster. Where have sailors claimed to have spotted this ship?
7 In how many coffins was the body of Lady Dering encased?
8 Ships with ghosts as 'passengers' are thought to have bad luck. What is the word to describe this?
9 What are Will-o'-the wisps?
10 The sudden hoot of an owl is said to be a warning. Of what?
11 The ghost of a bandit was said to have cured an insane boy in Mexico. Who was the bandit?
12 Poltergeist activity usually occurs when there are people of certain ages present. What are these ages?
13 The *Great Eastern* was thought to be jinxed. One of the construction crew had accidentally been sealed within the ship when still alive and his ghost was thought to bring bad luck on the ship. Where was his skeleton found and what was his trade?
14 What natural events sometimes make people think that a house is haunted?
15 What is the task of the graveyard guardian?
16 How did the owner of Rose Court kill herself?
17 When was Julius Caesar murdered?
18 What ghost-sensitive animals did an American ghost hunter take to investigate a haunted house in Kentucky?
19 What was the name of the phantom mongoose?
20 The spirit of an Indian girl, Silver Belle, appeared in front of a medium. How many people were witness to this weird event?
21 How many men were killed in the Battle of Shiloh in 1862?
22 After he was hung, what was Tom Colley's body suspended in?
23 How many people were interviewed in the ghost census of 1890?
24 What indian tribe hunted the rhea?
25 What is special about a camera loaded with infra-red film?
26 Why did Romans burn black beans?
27 What is the Brocken?
28 When was the main house of Surrenden Dering Manor burnt down?
29 What was the diet of the eating ghosts of the Banks Islands?
30 Strange ghostly tappings were heard in a house at Netherfield. What was their cause?
31 What sort of head was a khu thought to have?
32 The philosopher Athenodorus carried out what was, perhaps, the first piece of psychic research on record. The ghost was that of an old man. What colour hair did it have?
33 Where did the highwayman meet his painful end in Pluckley?

Answers

1 In France, near Beauvais.
2 It is claimed to have 12 ghosts.
3 Up to 200 metres high.
4 The way that a funeral procession is soon to pass.
5 In 2,000 BC.
6 Off the Cape of Good Hope.
7 Lead coffin in an oak casket. Seven.
8 To be jinxed.
9 Moving flames; sometimes seen in marshes.
10 A warning that death is about to strike.
11 Pancho Villa.
12 Between 12 and 16 years old.
13 The skeleton was found sealed between the inner and outer hull. He had been a riveter.
14 Creaking timbers; noises of small animals.
15 To keep away evil spirits and animals such as rats and mice.
16 She drank the juices of crushed poisonous berries.
17 March 15, 44 BC.
18 A rat, cat, dog and rattlesnake.
19 Gef.
20 18 people saw the appearance.
21 Over 24,000 men were killed.
22 A gibbet.
23 17,000 people were questioned.
24 The South American Lengua tribe.
25 It can take pictures in the dark.
26 To keep away ghosts called lemures.
27 The highest peak of the Harz mountains in West Germany.
28 In 1952.
29 People's souls.
30 An alarm clock.
31 That of a bird.
32 The ghost had grey hair.
33 He was speared to a hollow oak tree at Fright Corner.

Creepy quiz scorechart

33 correct. Excellent. 25 or more. Good. 15-25. Not so good. Below 15. Try again!

????

Are you a Mysteries of the Unknown Memory Master? Add up your Monster and Creepy quiz scores. Look at the chart below to see how you and your friends compare.

Number of correct answers		Percentage Score
	67	100%
	60	90%
	50	75%
	40	60%
	30	45%
	20	30%
	10	15%

ALL ABOUT UFO's

Although it looked like a weather balloon, this UFO, equipped with a box from which flashed orange-red lights, moved into, rather than with, the wind. Rex Pixley of California, USA, who saw the UFO, went and stood directly underneath as it hovered 6 metres up in the air. Suddenly the UFO rose up 30 metres and drifted slowly away.

Two men from Arizona, USA, claimed to have been captured in 1971 by creatures like this. One creature, 2.6 metres tall, is shown here operating a device which appeared to be used to process medical information. The men claimed they were taken aboard a huge flying saucer and examined with a probe linked, via this machine, to a giant computer.

In Spain, Raphael Jimenez and Manuel Perez were driving near Seville early one morning in 1969. They reported that they suddenly saw this flying saucer, glowing and flashing, sweep fast across the treetops ahead of them.

65

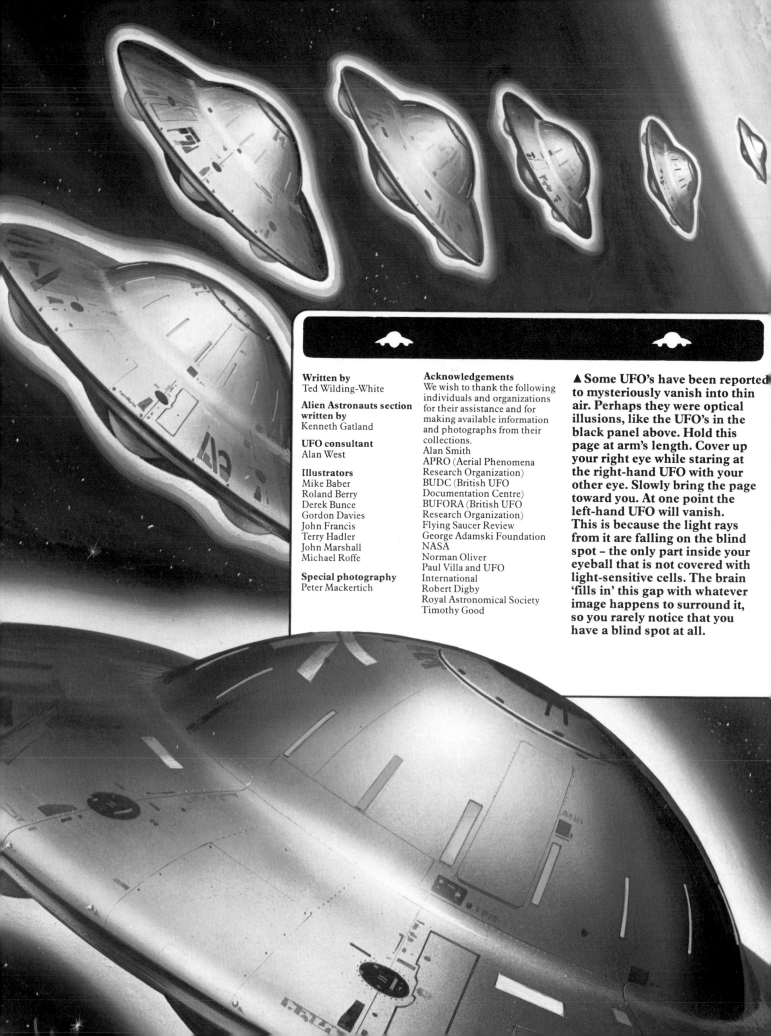

Written by
Ted Wilding-White

**Alien Astronauts section
written by**
Kenneth Gatland

UFO consultant
Alan West

Illustrators
Mike Baber
Roland Berry
Derek Bunce
Gordon Davies
John Francis
Terry Hadler
John Marshall
Michael Roffe

Special photography
Peter Mackertich

Acknowledgements
We wish to thank the following
individuals and organizations
for their assistance and for
making available information
and photographs from their
collections.
Alan Smith
APRO (Aerial Phenomena
Research Organization)
BUDC (British UFO
Documentation Centre)
BUFORA (British UFO
Research Organization)
Flying Saucer Review
George Adamski Foundation
NASA
Norman Oliver
Paul Villa and UFO
International
Robert Digby
Royal Astronomical Society
Timothy Good

▲ Some UFO's have been reported
to mysteriously vanish into thin
air. Perhaps they were optical
illusions, like the UFO's in the
black panel above. Hold this
page at arm's length. Cover up
your right eye while staring at
the right-hand UFO with your
other eye. Slowly bring the page
toward you. At one point the
left-hand UFO will vanish.
This is because the light rays
from it are falling on the blind
spot – the only part inside your
eyeball that is not covered with
light-sensitive cells. The brain
'fills in' this gap with whatever
image happens to surround it,
so you rarely notice that you
have a blind spot at all.

The world of UFO's

Contents

For centuries there have been reports of strange lights in the sky, weird craft landing on Earth, and even of living creatures emerging from them.

In recent years there have been more of these sightings than ever. Most of them are easily explained away by scientists, but some completely defy explanation.

What are unidentified flying objects? Could UFO's be hallucinations? Could they be spaceships from other worlds? Could they even be bizarre spectres from other dimensions in space and time?

The rest of this book gives you a glimpse into the weird world of UFO's. It describes reports, theories and possible explanations for them. Also included are sections on UFO hunting, UFO faking and a guide to the various things, both natural and man-made, which have been mistaken for UFO's.

What is a UFO?

History is full of stories of strange apparitions in the sky. But it was only after World War 2 that these sightings first attracted serious attention.

It all began on June 24, 1947. Kenneth Arnold reported seeing a formation of gleaming discs flying over the Rocky Mountains in North-West America. He described them as "skipping like saucers across water", and the name flying saucer quickly captured the public imagination. An official investigation adopted the more cautious name of Unidentified Flying Object. All strange sightings in the sky are called UFO's (pronounced You- Foes).

Once investigated, most UFO's turn out to be nothing of the kind. Others are given likely explanations. But for about one in five there has been no official explanation yet. They do not appear to be natural in origin – but they cannot be man-made either. For example, Arnold's 'saucers' were travelling at nearly twice the speed of sound in the days before the breaking of the sound barrier.

Some of these mysteries are probably hallucinations or hoaxes. Others may be explained by future scientific research. Another idea is that UFO's come from outer space.

▲ Kenneth Arnold was alone in his small aeroplane high among the Rocky Mountains in Washington State, USA, when he spotted nine 'saucers' flying in formation between distant peaks at about 1,900 kph. It became the first official UFO sighting.

All kinds of UFO

Although UFO's are popularly known as flying saucers, they come in a wide variety of shapes. The four most common of these are shown on the right, together with three shapes less often reported. UFO's appear to range in size from a few metres across to hundreds of metres. The pictures below are a guide only – there are many variations.

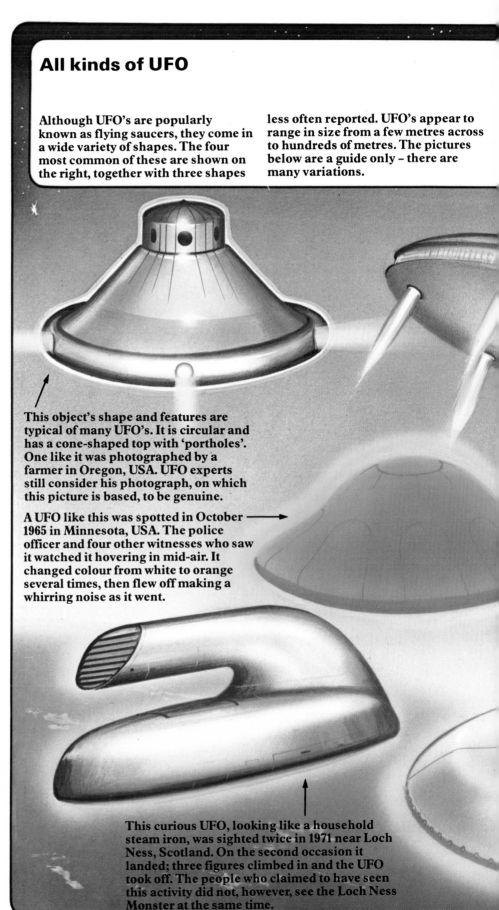

This object's shape and features are typical of many UFO's. It is circular and has a cone-shaped top with 'portholes'. One like it was photographed by a farmer in Oregon, USA. UFO experts still consider his photograph, on which this picture is based, to be genuine.

A UFO like this was spotted in October 1965 in Minnesota, USA. The police officer and four other witnesses who saw it watched it hovering in mid-air. It changed colour from white to orange several times, then flew off making a whirring noise as it went.

This curious UFO, looking like a household steam iron, was sighted twice in 1971 near Loch Ness, Scotland. On the second occasion it landed; three figures climbed in and the UFO took off. The people who claimed to have seen this activity did not, however, see the Loch Ness Monster at the same time.

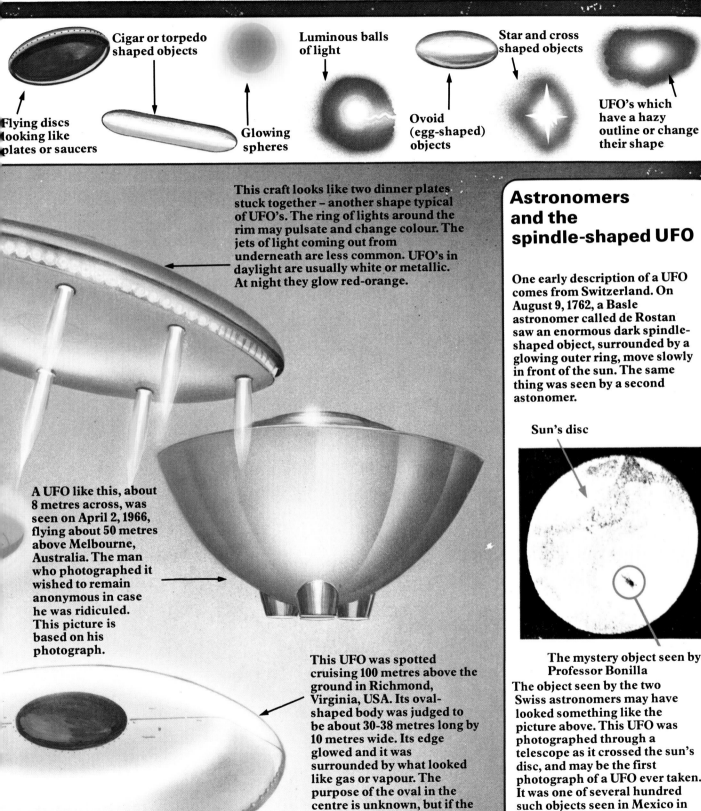

Flying discs looking like plates or saucers

Cigar or torpedo shaped objects

Glowing spheres

Luminous balls of light

Ovoid (egg-shaped) objects

Star and cross shaped objects

UFO's which have a hazy outline or change their shape

This craft looks like two dinner plates stuck together – another shape typical of UFO's. The ring of lights around the rim may pulsate and change colour. The jets of light coming out from underneath are less common. UFO's in daylight are usually white or metallic. At night they glow red-orange.

A UFO like this, about 8 metres across, was seen on April 2, 1966, flying about 50 metres above Melbourne, Australia. The man who photographed it wished to remain anonymous in case he was ridiculed. This picture is based on his photograph.

This UFO was spotted cruising 100 metres above the ground in Richmond, Virginia, USA. Its oval-shaped body was judged to be about 30-38 metres long by 10 metres wide. Its edge glowed and it was surrounded by what looked like gas or vapour. The purpose of the oval in the centre is unknown, but if the UFO were some sort of aeroplane it could well have been an air intake for engines.

Astronomers and the spindle-shaped UFO

One early description of a UFO comes from Switzerland. On August 9, 1762, a Basle astronomer called de Rostan saw an enormous dark spindle-shaped object, surrounded by a glowing outer ring, move slowly in front of the sun. The same thing was seen by a second astonomer.

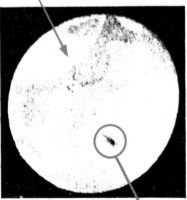

Sun's disc

The mystery object seen by Professor Bonilla

The object seen by the two Swiss astronomers may have looked something like the picture above. This UFO was photographed through a telescope as it crossed the sun's disc, and may be the first photograph of a UFO ever taken. It was one of several hundred such objects seen in Mexico in the early 1880s. The picture was taken from the observatory of Zacatecas in Mexico, by Professor Bonilla, on August 12, 1883.

UFO's in history

Did UFO's visit the Earth thousands of years ago?

Legends, signs and spectacular achievements, surviving from the days before history was written down, suggest that ancient man possessed knowledge which is lost to us. It has been suggested that creatures from other worlds could have been the teachers, the gods, even the ancestors of former civilizations.

Here are some examples of these early puzzles. Many, if not all, of them have explanations which are nothing to do with UFO's. It is the lack of proof either way which keeps their fascination alive.

▲ Hundreds of these stone giants stand half-buried on Easter Island in the Pacific Ocean. They weigh up to 50 tonnes and stand 10 or 20 metres high. Some researchers believe that they represent demonstrations of UFO technology. Thor Heyerdahl (who sailed across the Pacific Ocean in a raft called the Kon Tiki), made various experiments, both in constructing and in raising the giant statues. He concluded that it was possible for the islanders to have constructed them with no outside help at all.

Pyramid Power

Some researchers believe that the pyramids of Egypt were built with the help of advanced UFO science. There is no evidence for this, but the pyramids do contain mysteries which science has yet to explain. Experiments have been made with scale models of the 4,500 year old Great Pyramid of Cheops. Pieces of food placed inside dried out quickly and so were preserved instead of going mouldy. The plan shown here explains how you can make your own pyramid. When you have assembled it, try preserving a bacon rasher inside the pyramid and another in a shoe box. See whether the pyramid-shape preserves better than a box-shape.

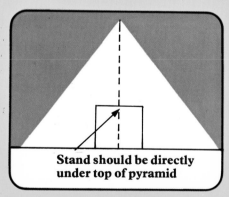

Stand should be directly under top of pyramid

▲ Use a compass to align your pyramid base exactly North-South and mark its position so you can lift it up occasionally to look at the bacon. Keep the bacon on top of the stand in the pyramid.

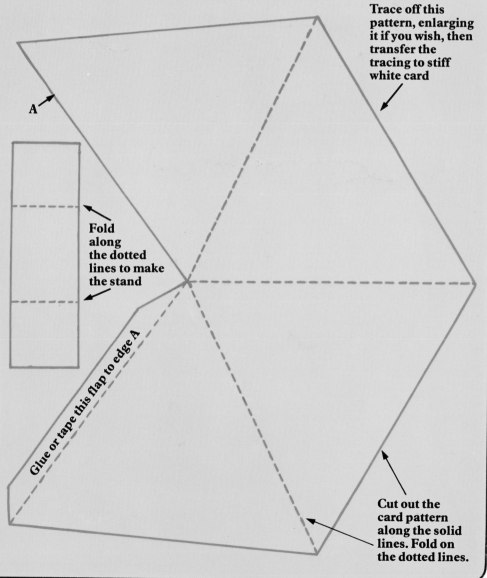

Trace off this pattern, enlarging it if you wish, then transfer the tracing to stiff white card

A

Fold along the dotted lines to make the stand

Glue or tape this flap to edge A

Cut out the card pattern along the solid lines. Fold on the dotted lines.

▲ At Nazca in Peru, South America, a plain 400 metres above sea level is cut by broad straight tracks up to 8 kilometres long. Seen from above they roughly resemble an airfield on which UFO's might have landed long ago. A ground plan of London's Heathrow airport is shown in the inset for you to compare. The construction of the tracks is very primitive – they are just cleared swathes on the rock surface. They may be connected with early astronomy, but it is unlikely they were built with the help of advanced UFO technology.

Prehistoric astronauts

Over the ages artists have depicted many images we cannot understand. A few of them show figures with strange features which, some say, are early man's attempts to portray UFO astronauts who visited them. But the fact they are unfamiliar to us is no evidence that they depict creatures from space.

▲ This ornate bronze statue, 60 centimetres high, was found in Japan. It looks like a figure in a space-suit with goggled helmet and equipment straps, but might as easily represent human armour, or some kind of ceremonial dress.

◄ A Mayan tomb, 1,300 years old, at Palenque, Mexico, is decorated with this complex design. It bears a curious resemblance to a creature operating a spaceship. From this angle it looks a little like a spacecraft taking off.

600 Years of UFO spotting

UFO spotting is nothing new, but the recording of reports is. Before the development of newspapers there were very few records of UFO activity.

This does not mean that UFO's never appeared, but only that few people could write down what they saw. That is why many early UFO reports come from monasteries, which were places of learning.

● On January 1, 1254, a mysterious coloured ship is supposed to have appeared over St. Albans in Hertfordshire, England. Its presence was recorded by the monks there.

● Then, in 1290, records tell us all activities at Bylands Abbey in Yorkshire, England, came to a standstill when a large silver disc flew slowly overhead.

● Very few cases were recorded over the next 400 years. But the expansion of newspapers and personal records in the 18th Century changed the situation. Here are some examples:

● London, England, December 11, 1741, 9.45 pm. Lord Beauchamp saw a small oval ball of fire descending from the sky. At a height of about 800 metres it levelled off and headed eastward, a long fiery tail trailing smoke, until it disappeared in the distance.

● London, England, March 19, 1748, 7.45 pm. Sir Hans Sloane saw a dazzling blue-white light with a reddish yellow tail dropping through the western evening sky. After half a minute it vanished into the dark landscape.

● Embrun, France, September 7, 1820. A stream of saucer-shaped objects crossed the town flying in formation. While over the town they changed course and made a perfect ninety-degree turn keeping to their strict formation.

● Niagara, USA, November 13, 1833. A large square luminous object hovered for more than an hour above the Niagara Falls.

Target Earth

1952 was a particularly good year for UFO sightings. As well as the 'Washington Invasion', described on the right, there were some 1,500 reports of UFO's that year in different parts of the world and more than 300 of them remain unexplained.

UFO's often occur in waves like this. The map below shows where and when such waves have taken place. Sometimes UFO activity is confined to particular regions, where people who have never heard of UFO's report an unusual number over a short period. Time of year also seems to play a part in the sightings—UFO's are particularly active in spring and there is a summer season in July.

Of course, newspaper reports contribute to the upsurge of UFO incidents. It is curious that even when there are many witnesses, accounts of one sighting may differ.

Once the idea of UFO's has been planted in people's minds they are more likely to start "meeting Martians" and their 'sightings' have to be treated with caution. Sometimes a UFO which mystifies a great many witnesses, and for which there appears to be no known cause, turns out to be man-made and easily explained. The 'UFO' over Lisbon, described on this page, is an example.

The Washington invasion

Place: Washington, USA
Date: July 19 and 26, 1952
Time: From 10.00 pm

One of the most famous of all UFO events is the so-called 'Washington Invasion'. One summer evening the citizens of the United States capital were treated to a display by five strange lights which manoeuvred for hours over the White House, the city and the countryside around.

A week later, the lights re-appeared. This time there were between 6 and 12 of them and they moved too fast to be aircraft.

Two F94 jet interceptors were scrambled to investigate them, but the pilots could find nothing and returned to base. However, when a third jet was sent up the pilot radioed that he was approaching a cluster of huge blue and white lights. As he closed in on them the lights moved to form a ring around him and travelled along with him for about 15 seconds before moving slowly away.

UFO Waves

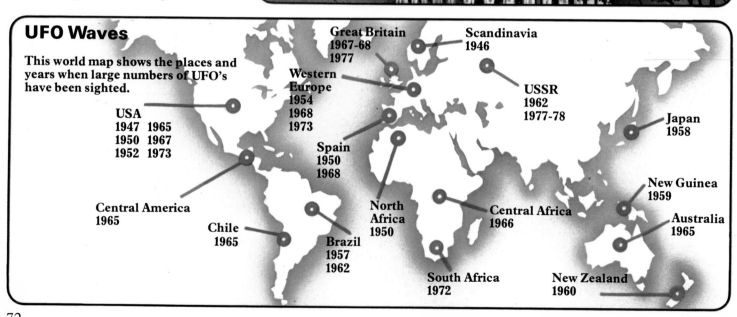

This world map shows the places and years when large numbers of UFO's have been sighted.

USA
1947 1965
1950 1967
1952 1973

Central America
1965

Chile
1965

Brazil
1957
1962

North Africa
1950

Spain
1950
1968

Western Europe
1954
1968
1973

Great Britain
1967-68
1977

Scandinavia
1946

USSR
1962
1977-78

Central Africa
1966

South Africa
1972

New Zealand
1960

Japan
1958

New Guinea
1959

Australia
1965

The flying cross

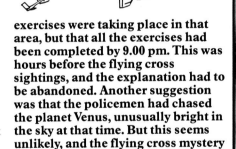

Place: Hatherleigh, Devon, England
Date: October 24, 1967
Time: 4.00 am

Police constables Roger Willey and Clifford Waycott were on routine night duty in their patrol car when they suddenly saw bright lights in the shape of a large cross pulsating in the sky ahead of them. As the patrol car drove towards it, the cross moved silently away. The policemen chased through the narrow lanes after it, but the cross always managed to accelerate away from them.

Eventually it moved off across the fields and the policemen gave up.

Once the sighting found its way into the papers, flying crosses were reported up and down the country. For a time it was thought the lighted 'cross' might be a tanker plane, like the one shown in the small picture above, surrounded by smaller aircraft on refuelling exercises. The British Defence ministry agreed that such

exercises were taking place in that area, but that all the exercises had been completed by 9.00 pm. This was hours before the flying cross sightings, and the explanation had to be abandoned. Another suggestion was that the policemen had chased the planet Venus, unusually bright in the sky at that time. But this seems unlikely, and the flying cross mystery has never been solved.

Airway intruder

Place: South of Lisbon, Portugal
Date: July 30, 1976
Time: 8.00 pm

A British Airways captain flying a Trident 2 was alerted by Air Traffic Control, Lisbon, to a brilliant white light "just sitting there" in the sky on the airliner's right hand side. As crew and passengers watched, two long cigar-shaped brownish objects, like thick vapour trails with solid centres, suddenly appeared below the light.

The sighting was publicized as an extraordinary UFO, until the Science Research Council, London, revealed what seemed to be the most likely cause. The 'UFO' was, in fact, a giant

research balloon at very high altitude, catching the light at sunset. The sun's rays reflected through the plastic fabric of the balloon to make it appear lit-up inside. The balloon had been launched in Sicily and was making its way to the United States, equipped with scientific instruments. By day the gas inside the balloon expanded, causing the balloon to rise, but at sunset when the gas cooled the balloon would sink.
To prevent it crashing, ballast was automatically dumped overboard each evening and it may have been this which the witnesses described as 'cigar shaped objects'. On the other hand, they may have seen clouds of fine steel shot which were released to measure wind-drift.

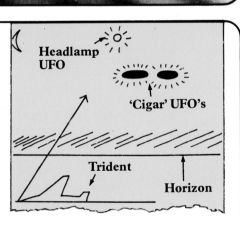

▲ This sketch is based on the Trident captain's drawing of the Lisbon 'UFO'. Notice the haze above the horizon after sunset, and the angle (arrowed) of the captain's view of the 'UFO'.

Close encounters

Close sightings fall into three classes. These were defined by Allen Hynek, an astronomer and UFO expert, who was a consultant to Project Blue Book, described on the page opposite.

The first kind of encounter occurs when a UFO is seen in the sky or on the ground. It becomes the second type of encounter if the UFO leaves evidence behind, such as holes in the ground

or burn marks on surrounding bushes. An encounter of the third kind occurs if creatures are seen, as in the case described below. Encounters of all three kinds are found on this page.

Encounter at Socorro

Place: Socorro, New Mexico, USA
Date: April 24, 1964
Time: 5.45 pm

In 1964, Project Blue Book recorded a new type of UFO event—the sighting of unidentified alien creatures.

Police Officer Lonnie Zamora, pursuing a speeding motorist among desert hills near Socorro, was distracted by a sudden roar and a bluish flame in the sky ahead. He left the road and drove up a rough hill until he spotted what he thought was an overturned car about 150 metres off the road.

The first UFOnauts

As he came closer he saw it was an oval, silvery object on four feet. It was marked with a red insignia. Two small human-like figures, wearing white garments similar to overalls, moved around near the object. Zamora approached them with the idea of helping, but as soon as the figures caught sight of him they seemed alarmed and jumped into their mysterious craft.

UFO blast-off

Zamora then heard a roar which grew louder and louder. A brilliant blue flame flashed from beneath the craft and the terrified policeman turned and fled as the object rose into the air. "I was scared of the roar," says Zamora. "I looked up and saw the object going away from me... The roar stopped. I heard a whine... then complete silence."

When UFO researcher Allen Hynek re-visited Socorro four months later he was struck by the illogical choice of the UFO landing sight and by the reliability of Zamora as a witness.

Unsolved mystery

The sighting has never been explained. The US Airforce put out a statement which implies the UFO could have been a test flight. But this seems unlikely, as no man-made oval object is so far known to have flown successfully.

▲ Shown above is the strange craft described by Lonnie Zamora. It was about five metres long and carried a sign which did not belong to any known air force. UFO's with insignia are rarely seen, and these markings have puzzled experts for years.

▼ This picture shows the landing site which was searched by Zamora and his police chief. They found four wedge-shaped prints of the UFO's 'feet' (arrowed in picture), footmarks and patches of burning scrub after the craft took off.

The night flier

Place: Marseilles, France
Date: October 1952
Time: 2.00 am

Shown on the right is the craft which customs officer Gabriel Cachinard said he saw at Marseilles Airport. He was sitting near the hangars when he noticed a light approaching from the left, low and silently at over 200 kph. It did not slow down smoothly—it just stopped dead on the runway. He walked towards it and, in the glow of the hangar lights, saw an object about five metres long and one metre high.

Shower of sparks

From 'windows' about 30 centimetres square came a pale light, changing from greenish to bluish. Then, while he was still 50 metres from the object, Gabriel saw a shower of sparks shoot out from underneath one end. It took off with a soft swish and vanished within seconds. There are few reports of UFO's landing at airports and this one is curious as the landing had no apparent purpose.

The radioactive egg

Place: Baltimore, Maryland, USA
Date: October 26, 1958
Time: 10.30 pm

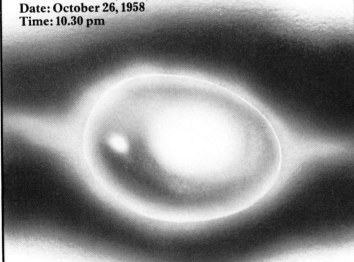

Two motorists turned a corner to see a glowing, egg-like object about 30 metres long hovering above a bridge 250 metres away. Their car stalled as they approached, and they hid behind it. 30 seconds later a brilliant light and a wave of heat flooded from the object accompanied by a thunderous roar. Then it shot upwards, vanishing in 10 seconds. Later, both motorists' faces showed signs of what doctors thought were radiation burns.

PROJECT BLUE BOOK

An official UFO investigation was begun by the US Air Force in 1947. Its purpose was to see if UFO's posed a security risk. The operation was named Project Sign. In 1949 it became Project Grudge and, in 1952, was renamed yet again to become Project Blue Book.

Unsolved mysteries

By 1969 about 40,000 reports had been investigated. Most were explained; some were guessed at; a few remained unsolved. Then the US Air Force ordered a special study of its collection to determine the value of further research into its UFO files for the advance of 'scientific knowledge.' This was called the Condon Report after Dr Edward Condon who headed it.

The files re-opened

Dr Condon concluded that the evidence did not justify further study of UFO's, and although his report came in for considerable criticism Project Blue Book was closed in 1969. Since then, so many UFO events have occurred that the Air Force is believed to have opened its files once more, this time as Project Old Blue Moon.

"Scramble...UFO!"

Every day air forces dispatch (or 'scramble') fighter jets to investigate suspicious radar signals. The target usually turns out to be an ordinary aircraft but occasionally it is thought to be a UFO. These UFO intruders escape at speeds so great no supersonic fighter can ever catch them.

Mantell's last flight

Place: Madisonville, USA
Date: January 7, 1948
Time: 2.00 pm

A huge object in the sky above Kentucky, USA, was seen by hundreds of people and three P-51 Mustangs were sent up to investigate it. After a few minutes one of the pilots, Thomas Mantell, radioed that it "appeared to be metallic." The other two pilots gave up the chase but Mantell decided to follow it up. He tried to reach 9,000 metres, but radio contact was lost abruptly. Later that day Mantell's aircraft was found completely destroyed 135 kilometres away. The press described Mantell as the first (and so far, the only) UFO 'victim.'

Star in the east

Place: Tehran, Iran
Date: September 9, 1976
Time: After midnight

A brightly lit object in the midnight sky over Tehran brought a flood of phone calls to Iranian Air Force Command. But it was 110 kilometres further north by 1.30 am when an F4 Phantom jet took off to investigate.

As the aircraft came within 50 kilometres of the target, radio contact with base suddenly ceased. The pilot quickly turned back and found that his radio started to work again, away from the UFO's influence.

Flashing coloured lights

A second Phantom (shown on the right), flown by Lt. Fafari, took off at 1.40 am. He approached the object at supersonic speed but the UFO accelerated away with lights flashing blue, green, red and orange in rapid succession.

Then a small brilliant object left the UFO and shot towards the Phantom. Fafari prepared to fire an AIM-9 missile, but before he could do so all weapon controls, instruments and radios failed.

Pursued by a UFO

He managed to dodge the object by diving steeply. It followed him for several minutes before returning to the 'mother ship.' Fafari then found his electrical systems were working again and he resumed the chase. He was able to pace the UFO but not catch up with it. The strange craft's size was difficult to tell because of its brilliance, but on Fafari's radar it looked about the same size as a 707 jet.

A UFO heads for Earth

Then another brilliant object detached itself from the UFO. This one dropped towards the Earth far below. It landed gently and its brightness lit up the landscape over an area of two or three kilometres. Fafari flew down and circled the dazzling light, noting its position. Then suddenly the object went dark. The Phantom returned to base, and as it landed a small cylindrical craft approached and passed overhead.

No trace

This last object was also seen by people on the airfield. But no trace of the shining landing craft was ever found. At first-light a search crew examined the area. The only evidence was a report by a local farmer of a loud noise and a light in the middle of the night.

UFO's over England

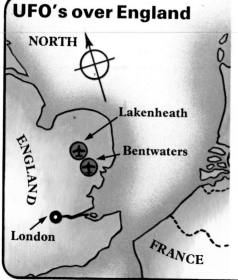

Place: Suffolk, England
Date: August 13, 1956
Time: From 9.30 pm

This story has become one of the 'classic' UFO sightings. Several objects were seen by many witnesses and were tracked on radar. They remain unexplained. The first UFO was sighted by a radar operator at Bentwaters, an air base in eastern England. It was just under 50 kilometres away when the radar picked it up. The UFO's speed was calculated to be over 8,000 kph—so fast that it should have produced a sonic boom. But the UFO travelled in complete silence.

▲ The radar operator then picked up an irregular group of 12 to 15 objects 13 kilometres south-west of Bentwaters. They were travelling north-east at about 150 kph and were led by three more UFO's flying in triangular formation.

▲ At about 10 pm a sergeant, who knew about the objects on the screen, was standing outside the control tower when he saw "a light the size of a pinhead" which hung in the sky for about an hour. But this light was later thought to be the planet Mars.

▲ A T33 two seater jet was sent up to investigate, but the pilot could see nothing unusual and the T33's own radar picked up no signals from the mysterious objects. After 45 minutes of fruitless search the jet returned to base. It looked as if the UFO's had disappeared.

▲ But at 10.55 a UFO crossed right over Bentwaters and was described by two witnesses as a "blurred light." People at the nearby base of Lakenheath watched as a low-flying object approached them, then apparently stopped in mid air. It disappeared and was never seen again.

Encounters in space

Perhaps the best place to see a UFO would be in outer space. There are many reports by American astronauts of puzzling objects and flashes of light, but none of these sightings is conclusive. The windows of a spaceship are very small and the pilot is often unable to give clear details of objects outside. Whether or not astronauts see them, Astronaut John Young is probably right to believe UFO's do exist. He said: "There are so many stars that it's mathematically improbable that there aren't other life sources in the Universe." You may agree with him when you read about life in outer space on page 88 .

Space hardware

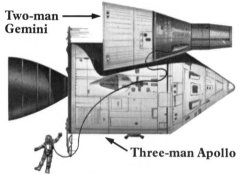

Two-man Gemini

Three-man Apollo

▲ The 10-mission Gemini programme was used to develop techniques for Moon flights. The Apollo spacecraft, designed especially for Moon missions, was also used in Earth orbit for the Skylab space station in 1973 and the joint Russian-American flight in 1975.

The egg in orbit

Place: Earth orbit
Date: June 1965
Time: 20th orbit

The first space UFO was seen by astronaut James McDivitt through the window of his Gemini 4 spacecraft. Early in the four-day mission, when his co-pilot Ed White was asleep, McDivitt glimpsed an object some 15 kilometres from the capsule which he described over his radio as having "big arms sticking out of it." He took pictures of the object before it disappeared, but curiously he was never able to find those pictures when the films were processed.

McDivitt's UFO

A short while later, a photograph appeared in the press which claimed to be 'McDivitt's UFO.' It showed an egg-shaped blob of light like the one in this picture, and though McDivitt denies that this is his missing photograph the incident was never cleared up. NASA, the American space agency, says the 'UFO' was glare reflected off a window bolt seen through the smudged pane.

Another suggestion

Another investigator suggests it was the Gemini's own Titan-2 second stage booster rocket in a nearby orbit. But the fact is that no-one really knows what McDivitt saw.

Apollo 11's UFO report

Place: Earth orbit
Date: July 1969
Time: Unknown

Some of the strangest sightings have been made during Apollo missions to the Moon. On the very first landing mission, Apollo 11, the crew spotted a large object flying in the same direction as themselves.

The object was too far away to be described clearly, but you can see an impression of it in this picture. Examined through a small telescope, it sometimes resembled a tumbling, hollow cylinder. But an adjustment of focus gave it a clear 'L' shape, "like an open suitcase," said Neil Armstrong.

The crew thought it must be their own cast-off S1V-B booster rocket, until told by ground control that the S1V-B was 10,000 kilometres away. One researcher has suggested the object was a fragment of insulation material.

The Apollo 12 crew reported a flashing object that accompanied them until it flew off at high speed.

Of all the theories as to how the Moon came into being, the most extraordinary comes from two Russian scientists, Mikhail Vasin and Alexander Shcherbakov. They suggest that the Moon is an artificial satellite – a huge ancient Noah's Ark of a spaceship – which was projected into Earth's orbit deliberately by creatures from another world when their own planet became impossible to live on. If this is so the Moon may be hollow, with a thick outer crust protecting equipment and perhaps even the remains of a whole civilization which was incarcerated for centuries inside. But there is slender evidence for this colourful theory and, until further proof emerges, the possibility that the Moon was once a spaceship stays remote.

IFO's – Identified Flying objects

Astronauts return to Earth with many pictures of the strange objects they have seen in space. Most of them are easily explained but a few escape identification for long enough to earn a reputation as UFO's.

The crew of Gemini 11 sighted a spacecraft miles from any position they thought one to be. Years later it was identified as a Russian satellite, Proton-3, which was in the last stages of its orbit before dropping lower into the Earth's atmosphere. It burned up 36 hours after the astronauts saw it.

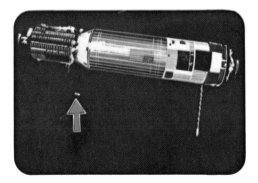

▲ One 'UFO' photographed from Gemini 12 turned out to be the Agena booster rocket. The small bright 'UFO' (arrowed), revealed by the photograph, is thought to be a reflection inside the camera lens.

▲ This distant object was also photographed during the mission of Gemini 12 through the open hatch door of the capsule. It was eventually recognised as a piece of rubbish from the Gemini craft itself.

Odd aircraft

Not all UFO's come from outer space. Aircraft engineers have designed lots of odd-looking machines which could easily be mistaken for alien craft.

Unfortunately for flying saucer enthusiasts, the disc-shape does not fly very well. In fact, the saucer shown in the big picture on the right wobbled so much that it had to be tied down with steel cables. Its safe flying height was only 1.22 metres off the ground.

Other designers have changed the disc-shape to an oval with better results, but it seems that ordinary aircraft with wings and a fuselage fly best of all.

▶ This flying saucer, called the Avro Avrocar, first flew in Canada in 1959. It was designed to take off vertically, fly at 480 kph, and be able to stop in mid-air to hover at any height. But the jet-powered craft was not a success, and the project was abandoned.

The saucer had three J69 jet engines arranged in a triangle around the central fan. The exhausts from the jets spun the fan.

The central fan, driven by the three jets, provided the lifting power for the saucer.

The two-man crew sat under bubble-shaped canopies either side of the machine. The pilot sat on the left, the observer on the right.

▲ This tiny plane, called the 'Fliegender Pfannkuchen,' was built in Germany during World War 2. Few details of this flying pancake are known. It was only a research machine equipped with a wooden propeller, and never went into active service.

The 'Flying Flapjack'

Single-seater cockpit

Engines buried in saucer shaped wing

Turbine propeller unit

This twin-engined plane was called the Chance Vought XF5U-I. It was designed to fly from American aircraft carriers. It could take off in very short distances–less than 60 metres–yet it could still fly at speeds over 600 kph.

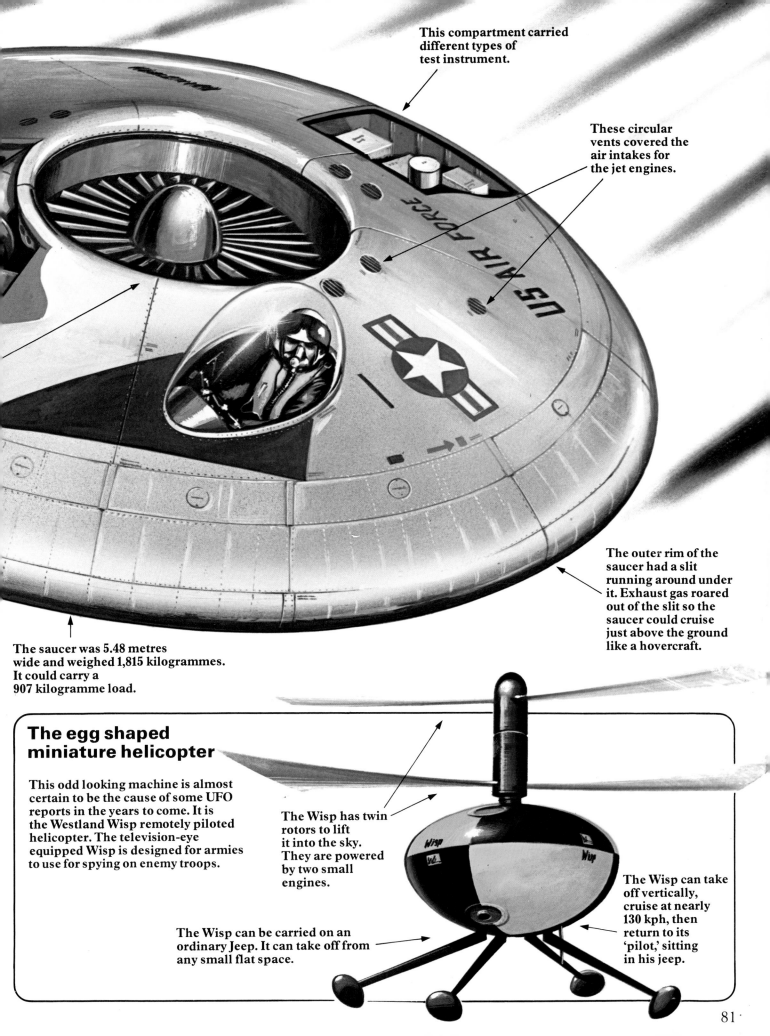

This compartment carried different types of test instrument.

These circular vents covered the air intakes for the jet engines.

US AIR FORCE

The outer rim of the saucer had a slit running around under it. Exhaust gas roared out of the slit so the saucer could cruise just above the ground like a hovercraft.

The saucer was 5.48 metres wide and weighed 1,815 kilogrammes. It could carry a 907 kilogramme load.

The egg shaped miniature helicopter

This odd looking machine is almost certain to be the cause of some UFO reports in the years to come. It is the Westland Wisp remotely piloted helicopter. The television-eye equipped Wisp is designed for armies to use for spying on enemy troops.

The Wisp has twin rotors to lift it into the sky. They are powered by two small engines.

Wisp

The Wisp can take off vertically, cruise at nearly 130 kph, then return to its 'pilot,' sitting in his jeep.

The Wisp can be carried on an ordinary Jeep. It can take off from any small flat space.

UFO's on the screen

Film makers have been building rockets and flying saucers throughout the 20th Century. Science fiction began on the screen in 1902 with 'A Trip to the Moon' by French film-maker Georges Meliés. But the first UFO appeared in 'The Airship Destroyers', made by Charles Urban in 1909. Some of the best early science fiction movies came from Germany. For one of them, 'The Girl in the Moon', a rocket was built which was so authentic that the film had to be destroyed. It was feared that foreign spies might make use of it. On this page you can see some of the famous film UFO's built since then.

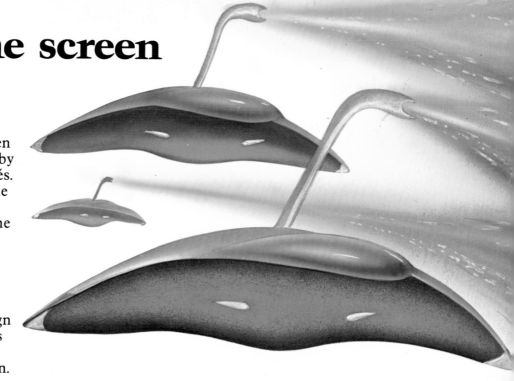

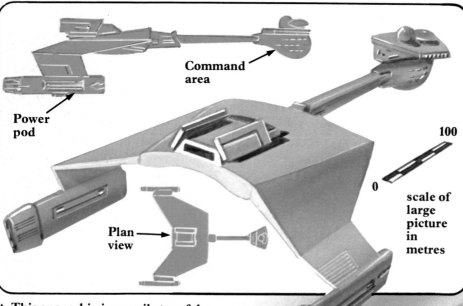

Command area

Power pod

Plan view

0 — 100

scale of large picture in metres

▲ These Martian war machines for the film 'War of the Worlds' were designed to be supported on pillars of electricity, but the million volts required were too dangerous. The final models were equipped with heat rays created by burning wire.

In the original book 'War of the Worlds' by H. G. Wells, the Martian war machines were like the three-legged mobile towers shown here. The tentacles held a box-like heat ray device.

▲ This spaceship is an evil star of the television series 'Star Trek'. In this programme the Earth crew of the spaceship 'Enterprise' explore the planets and peoples of the galaxy. They encounter the Klingons, a warrior race who fight for control of the galaxy in spaceships like the one above. Though Klingon warships appear huge they are, of course, only models.

▶ 'It came from Outer Space' was the name of a film made in 1953 about a UFO landing. The UFO was a huge sphere of hexagonal panels, illustrated right, which half-buries itself in the desert of Arizona in America. Alien creatures control local people to make them help repair the ship. The film used a special technique so that when you watched it through coloured spectacles the images looked three-dimensional.

Make your own UFO

Even though the secret of UFO propulsion has not yet been discovered, you can still fly your own UFO. All you need is a sheet of stiff card, tracing paper, a strip of balsa wood, sticky tape, glue and paint. Follow these measurements and you can make a UFO that really works.

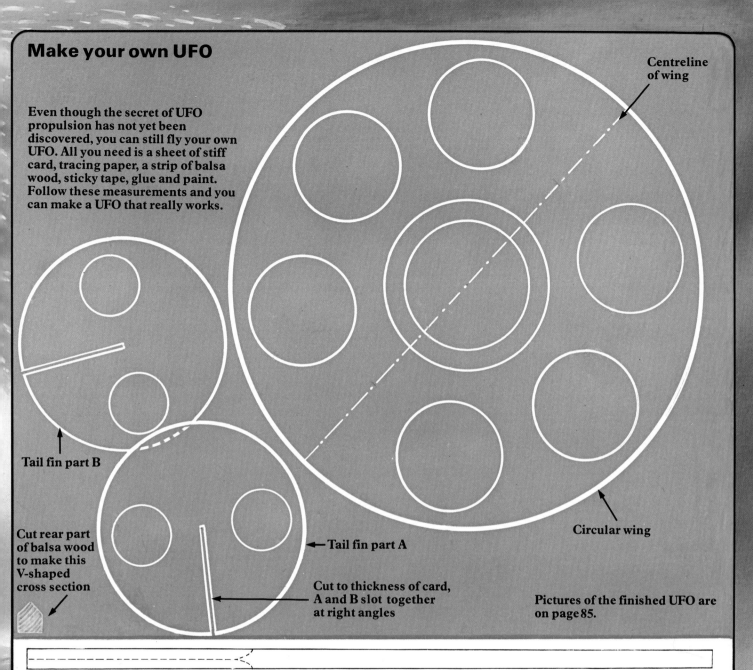

Centreline of wing

Circular wing

Tail fin part B

Cut rear part of balsa wood to make this V-shaped cross section

Tail fin part A

Cut to thickness of card, A and B slot together at right angles

Pictures of the finished UFO are on page 85.

— 57 mm —

You need a strip of balsa wood 6 mm x 6 mm x 192 mm long

Making the UFO

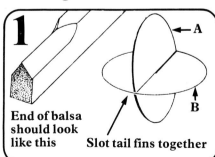

1

A

B

End of balsa should look like this

Slot tail fins together

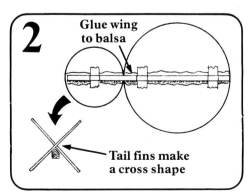

2

Glue wing to balsa

Tail fins make a cross shape

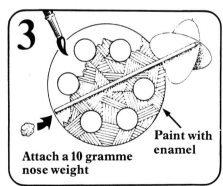

3

Attach a 10 gramme nose weight

Paint with enamel

▲ Trace the three discs on to the card. Make sure you transfer accurately the centreline on the large disc and the slot marks on the small ones. The two small discs slot together to make the tail unit. Cut out with a craft knife.

▲ Glue the untrimmed part of the balsa strip along the centreline of the large disc. The trimmed edge fits into the join of the tail unit where it is cemented. Make sure that the tail fins are at right angles to each other.

▲ Finally, add a nose weight of metal or plasticine. The UFO should glide in a smooth shallow dive. Adjust the nose weight until it does. You can make the UFO turn by bending the tips of the tail fins.

Hunting and faking

You might like to go UFO hunting for yourself. The best way to do this is to make a regular 'skywatch' from a hill or large open space. Take a note-pad, compass, pen, binoculars, a map and a loaded camera. Try and photograph your UFO first. Then write down as many details about it as you can. Take a friend with you, but do not compare notes until after you have made your report.

▶ **This UFO Report Form is based on those made by various UFO research organizations. It shows the kind of information you need for a proper investigation of any sighting. Copy it out and keep it in your UFO hunting kit to use as a guide.**

Fake photographs?

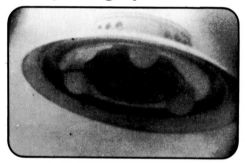

▲ This 'UFO' was photographed over California by George Adamski in 1952. Some have said it looks more like a picture of a chicken feeder than a flying saucer. Adamski claims he met a crewman from the UFO who told him the craft came from Venus.

UFO Report Form

1 Place ....
  Date ....
  Time ....

2 How long was ....
  UFO seen for? ....

3 Angle of UFO in the sky 90° 75° 60° 45° 30° 15° 0°
  (mark on with pencil)
  Position of UFO   N NW NE W E SW SE S
  Sketch UFO here

4 Appearance of UFO
  Shape ....
  Sound ....
  Colour ....
  Movements ....
  Number of objects ....
  Brightness ....
  (Compared to a star, Venus, Moon, Sun, etc.)

5 Name and address of witness (if any) ....

6 Weather conditions (Tick circle)

Clouds		Temperature		Wind		Precipitation	
Clear sky	○	Cold	○	None	○	Dry	○
Scattered cloud	○	Cool	○	Breeze	○	Fog or mist	○
Much cloud	○	Warm	○	Moderate	○	Rain	○
Overcast	○	Hot	○	Strong	○	Snow	○

Other conditions if any ....

▲ This photograph was taken in 1966 in Yorkshire, England. The photographer, Stephen Pratt, insists the picture is genuine. UFO experts doubt this because the UFO's are out of focus though the post and distant roofs are quite clear.

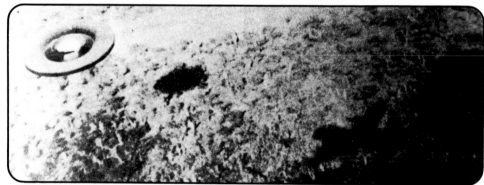

▲ An airline pilot of Avena Airways produced this picture in 1963. He claims he took it while flying over Venezuela. Perhaps you can see why it is a fake if you imagine yourself in the aeroplane taking the picture. The big shadow on the right is probably one of the engines. Compare the steep angle of the aeroplane shadow just in front of it with the position of the UFO in relation to its own shadow. The shadow ought to be tucked closer underneath the saucer.

1 Faking a UFO

It is not too difficult to fool your friends by taking fake UFO photographs, but there is little point in trying to fool the experts. They know any UFO photograph is only as good as the report which goes with it, and they have seen all the tricks before.

The pictures on this page are all fakes. They were taken to show how convincing a hoax can look, and illustrate some of the mistakes made by fakers in the past. In each case the 'UFO' is either a lamp-shade or the 'World of the Unknown' UFO described on page 83.

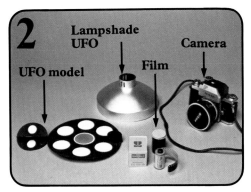

▲ The equipment used for faking is shown here. All you need is a camera, in this case a single lens reflex (but an ordinary instamatic camera will do), and reels of film. Most UFO pictures seem to be in black and white, but colour film was used for these photographs.

▲ The photographer chose a park on a hill, and took most of the pictures lying on his back. The UFO was thrown over his head and he photographed it as it flew. He was not always successful, as you can see: in this shot he photographed the thrower, too!

▲ The effects of 'shooting' into the Sun can be spectacular. The prism-like lights in the picture above are simply reflections in the lens of the camera itself. Here, the UFO looks as if it is about to make contact with its mother ship before speeding off into space.

▲ The picture on the left is the same UFO as in pictures two and three. The effect is caused as the craft flipped on its side, caught by the high wind which was blowing at the time. The picture on the right shows what might be called a close encounter with a jumbo jet.

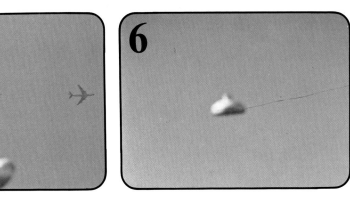

▲ This picture of the lampshade UFO shows an unforeseen hazard for the UFO faker. It looks like a rather bad photograph with a wire obviously holding up the UFO. In fact the 'wire' is the blue plastic tail of a kite which was flying 100 metres behind the UFO.

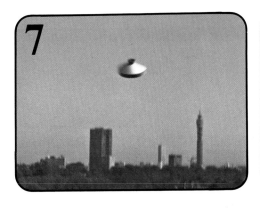

▲ This is probably the best picture of the day. The UFO is high in the sky with no possible means of support, and it is very difficult to tell how large it is. The camera followed the 'UFO' across the sky, blurring the background. Ask your friends to judge this shot—fact or fake?

▲ This menacing 'UFO' was actually photographed from indoors. The same camera and film were used, but the UFO was a paper shape, cut out and stuck on a window. The window was cleaned inside and out and the camera was held only 40 centimetres from the 'UFO.'

▲ The 6-centimetre 'UFO' was joined by another, again of paper but a different shape. UFO's look bigger and more realistic if the landscape is fairly distant, so keep foreground to a minimum. The sharper the UFO image, the nearer it looks.

Mistaken identity

The majority of UFO reports are traced, after careful examination, to objects or effects already known to man. This is quite understandable. If all sightings remained unexplained there would be just too many UFO's around to be convincing. It is the few that defy explanation which keep the experts thoroughly intrigued.

This page is a guide to some of the most common UFO illusions. You can use it to check any UFO's you might see. If your sighting fits none of these explanations it could be worth investigating further.

▲ Clusters of white lights, looking like alien craft, passed in V-formation over Lubbock, Texas, USA in 1951. The experts were foxed for years before they realized the 'craft' were flights of migrating geese. The city lights were reflected off their white bodies.

▲ Giant balloons are used to carry scientific instruments to the upper atmosphere. From 15-20 kilometres altitude the balloon is bathed in light even though the Sun has set on the Earth below. The aluminium fabric of the balloon shines brilliantly in the sky.

▲ Low cloud or fog can be highly reflective. If the source of light is concealed, as shown here, where a car is on the other side of the hilltop, headlights shining through cloud can create an uncanny glow in the sky. The lights change as the car moves.

▲ Ball lightning occurs rarely and little is known about it, but in thunderstorms you may see one or more luminous balls, 10 to 20 centimetres across, which crackle as they roll slowly across the sky. Ball lightning may vanish in seconds or linger for several minutes at a time.

▲ There are many different kinds of kites, from boxes and diamonds to deltas and bird-shapes. Even their tails can cause confusion as you can see on page 85. A recent American study of UFO sightings showed that two of the 800 reports investigated were kites.

▲ Parachutes, glimpsed as they drop through broken cloud, can be very deceptive. They are often used for dropping military supplies, and as some loads (such as the one above) require several parachutes, you may see odd shapes as the parachutes fall.

▲ The curved glass used in the windows of cars, trains and aeroplanes can reflect objects which are outside direct vision and distort them beyond recognition. You can experiment yourself with a glass jar and spoon, as shown in the picture.

▲ The hot exhaust of an aeroplane contains moisture which condenses in cold air. This forms long ribbons of cloud, called vapour trails. Broken up by the wind, such trails sometimes form cigar shapes and shine in the sun long after the ground is in darkness.

▲ Saucer-shaped clouds can be formed by rising air over hills. Known as lenticular (lens-shaped) clouds, they may appear both in clear and cloudy skies. They sometimes cluster in 'formations' like a colony of flying saucers.

▲ Comets are made of ice, rock and dust. As they approach the Sun they develop a shining tail which can be millions of kilometres long. Seen from Earth, most comets look like tiny smudges. But a few look like vast streamers hanging in the sky.

▲ Red, green or white signal flares are used by ships in distress, by soldiers on manoeuvres and at airports for signalling aircraft without a radio. Flares produce a bright light in the sky which sinks slowly to the ground. The light goes out as it hits the earth.

▲ A lighthouse uses a rotating beacon which produces a pattern of short and long flashes to warn ships away from dangerous rocks. The light code repeats itself every few seconds and is therefore easy to check. The light is usually low on the horizon and does not move.

▲ Points of light shooting across the night sky are usually meteors—rocks and stones from space which burn up in the atmosphere. The Earth runs into several belts of meteoroids regularly each year, and in August and November meteor showers are very common.

▲ Even the familiar Moon may be unrecognizable at times, and is responsible for up to 5 percent of UFO sightings. When it is partially obscured by cloud or by the horizon, the parts which remain visible can look quite unfamiliar, both in colour and shape.

▲ 17 percent of 'UFO' sightings are identified as low-flying aircraft. At night a plane displays this light pattern: red on the left wing-tip, green on the right and white on the tail. You may see a red flashing beacon, a floodlit tail and head-lights as the plane comes in to land.

▲ Stratus cloud, which produces a heavy grey sky, can be thin enough for the Sun to shine through it. But the image is diffused and distorted, and our familiar Sun is transformed into an eerie light glowing through the cloud in the daytime sky.

▲ The planet Venus is the most common UFO mistake of all. With other astronomical objects, it is responsible for 27 percent of all UFO's which have been identified. It is the brightest object in the sky after the Sun and Moon.

Life in outer space

If UFO's do come from other worlds, these worlds are probably elsewhere in our galaxy.

All the stars you can see in the night sky belong to our own galaxy, called the Milky Way . It is pictured here—a huge whirlpool of stars, gas and dust slowly turning in space. Our Sun, an ordinary star with a family of planets, is about two-thirds away from the galaxy's centre. There are more then 100,000 million stars in the galaxy and many of these could have life-bearing planets in their own solar systems. The Milky Way is just one in millions of galaxies, so it is very likely that intelligent creatures somewhere are pondering the same question as we are: is anyone there?

This tiny circle shows (to scale) how far radio signals from Earth have travelled out into the Galaxy. You can see from the size of the galaxy that they have barely made a start. One way to find other civilizations is to look for the radiation they send out—particularly the radio signals. If advanced civilizations are beaming signals our way, and the signals have reached the solar system, radio telescopes should be able to pick them up.

Origins of life

After the Sun and planets had formed from interstellar gas clouds, the Earth's internal heat caused the surface to melt and throw out huge quantities of gas and water vapour. This atmosphere was rich in hydrogen and contained many kinds of chemical molecules which reacted together in sunlight and were deposited as a 'soup' in shallow seas. In time, amino acids and protein formed, and life began to develop. This process is extremely complex, but there are 100,000 million stars in the Milky Way and many huge galaxies lie beyond, so it seems very unlikely that Earth is the only planet in the universe on which there is life.

The Milky Way is about 100,000 light years across. A light year is the distance light travels in a year—nearly 9,500,000 million kilometres, or over 299,270 kilometres each second. Radio waves travel at the same speed.

Stars within calling distance

This diagram shows how far radio signals from Earth have travelled into space. The stars illustrated are of a similar type to our Sun. If they have planets, life could have evolved there.

Proxima Centauri

Earth

Alpha Centauri

0

Barnard's Star

10

GLOBAL TV

Tau Ceti

Epsilon Eridani

SPACE TRACKING RADAR

70 Ophiuchi

Eta Cassiopeiae

POWERFUL DEFENCE RADAR

36 Ophiuchi

20

Beta Hydri

Zeta Hercules

Mu Hercules

30

Eta Bootes

WORLD WAR 2 RADAR

Beta Gemini

Alpha Bootes

FIRST TV BROADCASTS

40

EARLY RADIO

Alpha Aurigae

Eta Cepheus

Gamma Cepheus

50

Theta Centaurus

Sigma Libri

Beta Ceti

60

Eta Serpens

Distance from Earth in light years

One day another civilization may pick up the radio, radar and space communications from Earth. Weak signals from the early days of broadcasting have already reached stars 50 light years away. Stronger signals from our radars and television transmitters are following. Creatures from other worlds may be attracted here to investigate.

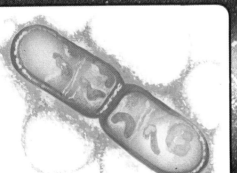

▲ This rare Earth organism, which is shown here dividing in two, is proof that life can exist under very harsh conditions. It was found thriving in surroundings which may be similar to the thick atmosphere of Jupiter.

Listening to the sounds of space

Earth scientists are already probing the nearer stars for signals that might be coming from other civilizations. The quest began in 1960 When Dr Frank Drake began his Ozma experiment named after the fairy-tale kingdom of Oz. Using a 25.9 metre wide radio telescope at Green Bank, Virginia, USA, Drake recorded radio waves from the stars Tau Ceti and Epsilon Eridani—but heard no tell-tale signals from other civilizations.

Astronomers are now studying star clusters and other galaxies as well as individual stars.

▲ An even larger radio telescope is now being used at Green Bank in a new investigation of Sun-type stars.

UFOnauts

There are two main theories about UFO's. One is that they are spaceships piloted by creatures from other worlds. The other is that they are hallucinations. Most sightings seem to be of man-shaped creatures or monsters from myths and legends. In fact, scientists think real space visitors would be most unlikely to look like men. Their evolution would have taken an entirely different course. If UFO's do exist, where might they come from? There are many sun-like stars within 60 light years of Earth. Any of them could have planets, perhaps with creatures living on them.

Encounters of the third kind

The tiny goblin-creature on the right was one of five apparently seen in 1955 by a farming family in Kentucky, USA. When the farmers shot at it they heard a metallic sound but the creature seemed unhurt. A few minutes later it peered in through one of the farmhouse windows and, when one of the farmers ventured outside, "a silvery hand...inquisitively brushed the man's hair." The creature became known as the 'Kelley-Hopkinsville Goblin.' The figure on the far right was reported near Zafra, south-west Spain, in 1968. It was two metres tall, had long arms and glowing green clothing.

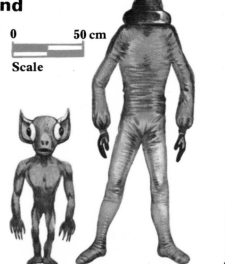

0   50 cm

Scale

Is this the home of the Hopkinsville goblin?

It is difficult to believe that the 'goblin' really exists; but just suppose it does, what sort of world might it live on? Its planet could circle one of the nearer Sun-like stars, perhaps Eta Cassiopeiae A (see chart, page 89). This star, only slightly smaller than our Sun, has a small companion star which takes some 480 years to move round it. At certain periods, creatures living on a planet of the main star would see two suns in the sky. The main star is yellow with a greenish tinge, the other orange-red and much further away.

The goblin's fairly light build could mean that its world is smaller than ours and has less gravity. The planet would therefore have a thinner atmosphere, so the creature's chest—and lung capacity—would need to be large.

More of the radiation from the world's suns will reach the planet's surface if the atmosphere is thin so the goblin could have a dark pigmented skin. As sound travels badly in thin air it would have large ears. The farmers described their 'goblin' as having large eyes. This might suggest its natural surroundings are gloomy—perhaps the goblin's world is further away from the sun, and therefore much colder than Earth.

The tiny far-off companion star, Eta Cassiopeiae B, is already high in the sky, but casts little light and no warmth.

The 'morning star'—our own Sun—is still visible in the fading night sky. It is 19 light years away.

One of the spacecraft of the Goblin community rises at the head of a laser-like power beam. All the power equipment is under the circular take-off platform.

It is dawn as the star Eta Cassiopeiae A rises to warm the icy wastes of the goblin world.

This radar dish, though oddly proportioned, serves the same purpose as its counterpart on Earth, so its shape is very similar.

Even icicles are long and thin in the low gravity.

Even stranger creatures

Biologists believe life-forms on other planets could be very different from life on Earth. Man breathes a mixture of nitrogen and oxygen. But the inhabitants of other planets might breathe a different mixture.

The creature on the right is a kind of walking octopus. Arms and legs are interchangeable; eyes are on stalks; brain and stomach are both inside the body, with the mouth underneath. The 'hands' have no thumbs but are simply ropes of muscle.

This gas-bag creature might live in the atmosphere of a giant planet similar to Jupiter. It sucks in hydrogen gas and then contracts to squirt the gas out of its tail. It moves in spurts by jet reaction.

It is possible that insect-like creatures, like the one here, might have reached a much higher level of intelligence on other planets than they have on Earth.

Flying creatures would need a large wing-span in the thin air. These look like delta-wing versions of Earth's prehistoric pterosaurs.

In the sky is an orbiting space colony. Millions of goblins could live in space to exploit natural resources on moons and asteroids of their solar system. They manufacture all their needs in space factories, leaving the Goblin world unpolluted by factory smoke and fumes.

Vegetation looks strange to human eyes. The plants appear top-heavy. This is because the planet's gravity does not drag on them as much as gravity pulls at plants on Earth. Leaves are disc- shaped, turning to follow the feeble sunlight.

It was not clear from the Kentucky farmers' reports whether the goblin wore clothes. Back on its icy home world it would probably need them.

Starflight

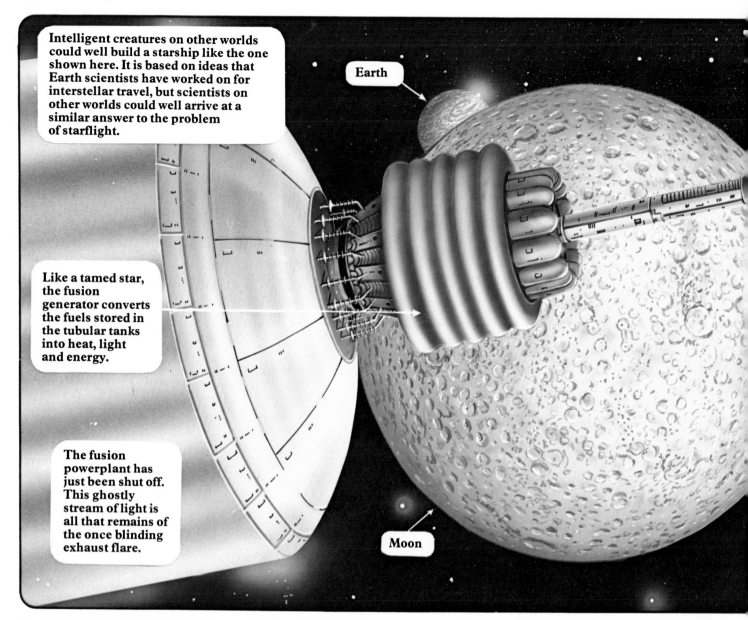

Intelligent creatures on other worlds could well build a starship like the one shown here. It is based on ideas that Earth scientists have worked on for interstellar travel, but scientists on other worlds could well arrive at a similar answer to the problem of starflight.

Earth

Like a tamed star, the fusion generator converts the fuels stored in the tubular tanks into heat, light and energy.

The fusion powerplant has just been shut off. This ghostly stream of light is all that remains of the once blinding exhaust flare.

Moon

It should not be surprising if advanced civilizations in other parts of the Universe have discovered how to travel between the stars. Earth scientists have already studied the problem. One idea for a starship is the photon rocket, shown in the picture above. The rocket exhaust is a blinding cone of radiation which would enable the ship to travel near to the speed of light, and so make interstellar journeys possible. Such a starship, in Earth orbit, might be the 'mother' of the UFO's which are said to invade Earth's atmosphere. People have described going aboard them and talking with their crews.

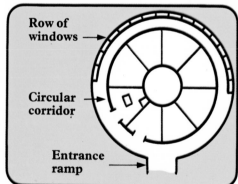

Row of windows

Circular corridor

Entrance ramp

▲ While driving through New Hampshire, USA, in 1961 Betty and Barney Hill claimed to have 'lost' two hours of their lives after seeing a UFO. Later, under hypnosis, Betty described meeting humanoids aboard the craft. Barney drew this plan of the interior.

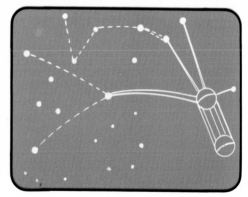

▲ While she was hypnotised Betty said she had been shown a star chart by the UFO's leader. Later, she sketched a map which showed trade routes (heavy lines) between star colonies and expedition routes (dotted lines). Names of stars were added to match known star patterns.

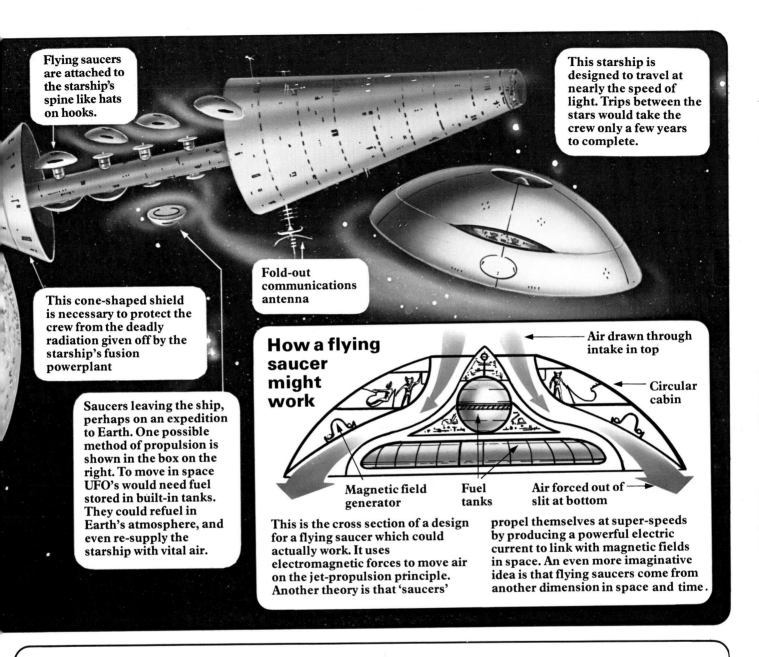

Flying saucers are attached to the starship's spine like hats on hooks.

This starship is designed to travel at nearly the speed of light. Trips between the stars would take the crew only a few years to complete.

This cone-shaped shield is necessary to protect the crew from the deadly radiation given off by the starship's fusion powerplant

Fold-out communications antenna

Saucers leaving the ship, perhaps on an expedition to Earth. One possible method of propulsion is shown in the box on the right. To move in space UFO's would need fuel stored in built-in tanks. They could refuel in Earth's atmosphere, and even re-supply the starship with vital air.

How a flying saucer might work

Air drawn through intake in top

Circular cabin

Magnetic field generator

Fuel tanks

Air forced out of slit at bottom

This is the cross section of a design for a flying saucer which could actually work. It uses electromagnetic forces to move air on the jet-propulsion principle. Another theory is that 'saucers' propel themselves at super-speeds by producing a powerful electric current to link with magnetic fields in space. An even more imaginative idea is that flying saucers come from another dimension in space and time.

UFO's – fact or fiction?

It is best to look for a simple explanation before jumping to the conclusion: "I've seen a UFO!" The chart on the right is based on information from the US Air Force Blue Book of UFO sightings between 1963 and 1967. It shows that most UFO's can be put down to wrongly identified familiar objects, and undoubtedly many of the 'unexplained' sightings could be put into the 'explained' category if there was more known about them. What of the people who believe they have actually met visitors from space? Does the human brain create them like the characters met in dreams, or

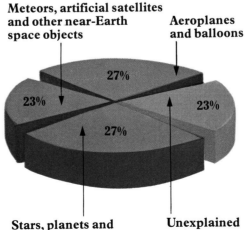

Meteors, artificial satellites and other near-Earth space objects

Aeroplanes and balloons

27%

23%

27%

23%

Stars, planets and other astronomical objects.

Unexplained sightings

could they be real?

There is little or no hard evidence for their existence. It is curious that if UFO's piloted by creatures from space are investigating Earth they have not appeared to more people or tried to make formal contact with man. They have come a very long way, possibly travelling for years to reach Earth, and it seems unlikely that they would content themselves with a brief sight-seeing visit. Until a UFO lands in a major city, is photographed and the crew interviewed, there is no way to prove that they exist.

The amazing world of UFO's

UFO stories, like fishermen's tales, may become exaggerated in the telling. But even if they are only partly true, they still suggest that amazing things are happening in the world. You can read about some of them on this page.

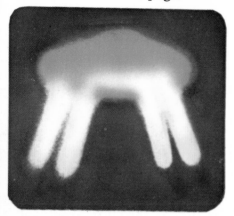

French UFO researcher Jean Bedet found this picture pinned with a note to his car windscreen one day. The note explained that the photograph was taken near Albiosc in the Vosges mountains in France at 11.30 pm on March 23, 1974, by a witness who insisted on remaining anonymous.

He was a doctor, who had seen the saucer as he was driving home late at night along a deserted country road, after visiting a patient. The four white glowing bars at the base of the craft are thought to be either rays of light or landing gear. Though he was the only witness who photographed it, the anonymous doctor was not the only person to whom the saucer appeared. A similar craft was reported at the nearby village of Thillot, and about 300 kilometres away in the Swiss village of Taverna.

In Sweden alone there were about 1,000 UFO reports in 1946. Most of the reports concerned 'rocket-shaped' objects, which have never been identified.

UFO's are most often seen between the hours of 9.00 pm and 10.30 pm.

A public opinion poll carried out in the USA in January 1974 showed that more than one in ten of the people questioned claimed to have seen a UFO.

The UFO speed record is held by a saucer seen flying over South America in January 1977. Its speed was calculated to be about 28,000 kph – the same speed as an artificial satellite orbiting Earth.

In the Autumn of 1967, Canadian Maritime Command was alerted by an object bearing several coloured lights which was flying over the North Atlantic. It glided with a whistling noise into the sea. But when the search party arrived there was no sign of any debris floating in the water, and divers searching the sea bed could find no wreckage of any kind.

In the last 30 years over 100,000 people have reported UFO experiences.

On June 16, 1963, Paul Villa received a message from space. The creatures who contacted him had worked out how to use Earth radio and telephone systems and Paul Villa claims they had selected him to do some 'public-relations' work for them. They told him that if he went to a place 15 miles from Albuquerque, New Mexico, at 2.00 pm that day he

would be able to photograph their spacecraft as it landed. He did so, taking 7 pictures, and the photograph above is one of them. When the saucer landed, Paul Villa spent an hour and a half talking to the creatures which had contacted him. They were male and female, similar to humans but far more advanced, and "very beautiful".

They told him that they could travel faster than the speed of light, making the journey from their home in another galaxy in a very short time. Their purpose in contacting him was to inform the human race of their existence – but gradually, so that Earth people might get used to the idea of life on other worlds. The story is a good one, but it is probably not true. Photographic experts who have examined the pictures declare them to be fakes.

Imagine his surprise when a young Belgian miner looked out of his window and saw a UFOnaut collecting stones from his own back yard. The miner watched in amazement as the creature finished its task and walked towards the wall at the end of the yard. The miner expected the creature to climb the wall or vault over it, but it did neither. It simply walked up the side of the wall like a human spider, so that its body was level with the ground.

When it reached the top of the wall its body swung over until it was facing the ground on the other side. Then it disappeared from view. Shortly afterwards a UFO zoomed off into the sky.

UFO's have been reported from every country in the world. News of them flows in steadily at an average of 40 sightings every day.

In the early morning of June 17, 1957, a US Airforce RB 47 jet was chased by a UFO for well over 1,100 kilometres.

For an hour and a half, as they flew from Mississippi through Louisiana and Texas into Oklahoma, the 6-man crew attempted to outwit the UFO using the jet's complex electronic equipment. The most curious fact about the UFO was that it seemed to play 'hide and seek'. It was not simply that the crew could see it one minute and not the next – the UFO also vanished from the aircraft's radar screen, and from the ground control radar which was tracking it, only to re-appear moments later. This ought to be impossible. Perhaps the UFO was moving in and out of our universe like a stone bouncing across the surface of a pond.

14-year old Alan Smith took this extraordinary picture of a UFO on August 2, 1965, at Tulsa, Oklahoma, USA. The odd light grouping is unique in UFO sightings.

94

A dictionary of UFOlogy

Ufology is the name given to the subject of UFO's and everything connected with them. People who study it are called Ufologists. This dictionary includes words about space and Ufology which are not fully explained elsewhere in the book.

ALIEN   Any creature unknown on Earth and therefore possibly from another world. It also refers to any suspected life in outer space.

ASTRONAUT   Human space traveller. It comes from Latin and Greek words meaning 'star sailor.' Another word (usually used of Russian astronauts) is cosmonaut, meaning 'sailor of the universe'.

EXTRA-TERRESTRIAL   Refers to anything which originates outside Earth, such as an alien creature.

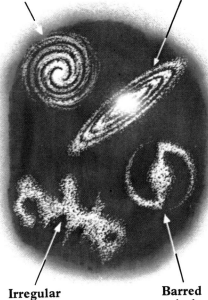

Some types of galaxy: Spiral, Elliptical, Irregular, Barred spiral

FLYING SAUCER   The popular descriptive name for a UFO. It was introduced by Kenneth Arnold when he described his own sighting in 1949, but it is also applied to UFO's which are not circular.

GALAXY   Gigantic cluster of stars, of which there are millions throughout the Universe. Our Sun is in the Milky Way galaxy, which is about 100 million light years across.

HUMANOID   A creature resembling the human form, standing upright with two arms, two legs and a head.

INTERSTELLAR   The space between the stars.

LASER   A device for producing concentrated light rays in a very narrow beam. The letters stand for Light Amplification by Stimulated Emission of Radiation.

LIGHT YEAR   The distance light travels in a year, 9,460,000 million kilometres. The speed of light is 299,270 kilometres per second.

METEOROID   A lump of space debris. If a meteoroid hits Earth's atmosphere it usually burns up and is seen as a meteor. If it remains intact and hits the Earth itself, it is called a meteorite.

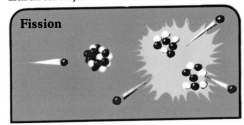

Fission

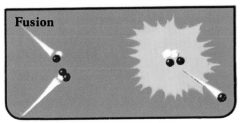

Fusion

NUCLEAR REACTION   Fission or fusion of atoms, as illustrated above. Fission means splitting the atoms. Fusion means merging two atoms into a single heavy atom. In both cases energy is given off in the form of light, heat and radioactivity. The Sun and all other stars burn by the fusion process. In controlled form, nuclear reactions can help generate electricity. They are also used as the source of power for atomic bombs.

ORBIT   The curving path of one body as it moves around another, such as the Moon moving round the Earth.

PHOTON   A particle of light.

RADAR   Device which uses radio signals to detect far-off objects. The signals are beamed out by a transmitter. They bounce off objects in their way and the returning 'echoes' are displayed as blips on a TV-like screen.

RADIATION   The transmission of any form of energy, such as light, heat or radio waves.

RADIOACTIVITY   Nuclear energy given off by some elements (for example, uranium). Too much radioactivity is highly dangerous to living things.

RADIO TELESCOPE   A telescope, usually bowl shaped, designed to catch radio waves from space which are not detectable on ordinary optical telescopes.

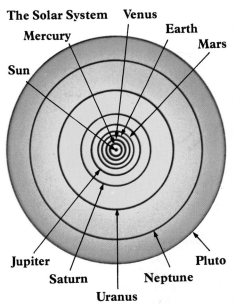

The Solar System: Sun, Mercury, Venus, Earth, Mars, Jupiter, Saturn, Uranus, Neptune, Pluto

SOLAR SYSTEM   The Sun, with its family of nine planets moving in orbit around it, is called the solar system. Earth is the third closest planet to the Sun, as you can see from the diagram above. Other stars may be circled by planets and so have planetary systems of their own.

STAR   A large body in space which generates its own light. The Sun is the closest star to Earth. All others are far away in the Milky Way and beyond.

UFO ENCOUNTER   UFO expert Alan Hynek graded UFO sightings into three types of 'encounter.' The first is merely a sighting in the sky or on the ground. For the second, the UFO must react to the witness in some way, land or leave signs that it really existed. Encounters of the third kind involve the appearance of alien beings. Examples of all kinds appear on page 74 ·

UFONAUT   Alien creature which might be one of the crew of a UFO.

Further into the unknown

If you want to explore further into the unknown, you will need a way of storing information.

One of the best methods is to start a file of press cuttings. Whenever a mystery event is reported in a newspaper or magazine, cut out the story and file it. The file can be a scrapbook or better still, a loose-leaf box file, which you can get from any good stationery shop. The advantage of a box file is that you can put in and take out information as and when you please.

Arrange the entries by date, place or subject. You could divide it into sections like this book. Make sure that you stay with the same system so that you can look up and add entries quickly and easily.

If you want to look around or photograph the scene of an unusual happening (ghost, monster or UFO) make sure you ask the owner's permission first. Most people are glad to help if you ask them but they do not like strangers trespassing on their property.

The list below is a small selection from the many monster books available. Tim Dinsdale's book gives a very interesting background to the lake monsters of Scotland. L B Halstead's book is one of the best on dinosaurs. It is very detailed and gives all the latest information on prehistoric monsters. If you are interested in the bizarre creations of ancient Greek myth, then the *Odyssey* is well worth a read.

Vampires, Zombies, and Monster Men/Monsters and Mythical Beasts
Daniel Farson and Angus Hall (Aldus/Jupiter)
Monsters and Mysterious Beasts
Carey Miller (Piccolo)
Heroes and Monsters Retold by James Reeves (Blackie)
Bigfoot John Napier (Abacus)
The Book of Imaginary Beings
J L Borges (Jonathan Cape)
A Book of Dragons Roger Lancelyn Green (Puffin)
The Story of Loch Ness Tim Dinsdale (Target)
In Search of Lake Monsters
Peter Costello (Panther)
In the Wake of the Sea Serpents
Bernard Heuvelmans (Rupert Hart-Davis)
The Evolution and Ecology of the Dinosaurs L B Halstead (Peter Lowe)
The Children's Picture Prehistory: Dinosaurs Anne McCord (Usborne)
Translations of **Beowulf** and Homer's **Odyssey** are published by Penguin

The chances of encountering a ghost are rather slim – even psychic researchers rarely claim to see them. But 'armchair ghost-hunting' can be spine-chilling enough. The books below and in the next column are a mixture of fictional ghost stories and non-fiction books describing real events and modern researches into the world of the supernatural.

The 1st Armada Book of True Ghost Stories Christine Bernard (Armada)
Ghosts Jane Bord (David and Charles)

Ghosts and Hauntings
Aidan Chambers (Longman Young)
Great Ghosts of the World
Aidan Chambers (Piccolo)
Ghostly Experiences and **Ghostly Encounters** Susan Dickinson (Lion)
Ghosts, Ghosts, Ghosts
Ruth Fenner (Chatto and Windus)
Ghosts and Spirits of Many Lands
Edited by Littledale Freya (Target)
Ghosts – the Illustrated History
Peter Haining (Sidgwick and Jackson)
The Hag of the Dribble and Other True Ghost Stories Bernhardt J Hurwood (Robert Hale)
The World of Ghosts
Alan C Jenkins (Chatto and Windus)
The Haunting and the Haunters
Kathleen Lines (Bodley Head)
The Realm of Ghosts Eric Maple (Pan)
Ghosts, Spooks and Spectres
Charles Molin (Puffin)

A farm manager and his nephew claimed to have seen a UFO like this flying over Argentina in 1971.

Many UFO books make wild claims, but show little or no evidence to back up their authors' ideas. For a cool look at UFO's in general, try *UFO's and Other Worlds* by Peter Ryan (Kestrel). A book which shatters most of the 'prehistoric astronaut' theories is *The Past is Human* by Peter White (Angus and Robertson). For a general view of man and the universe read *The Cosmic Connection* by scientist Carl Sagan (Fontana). There are many UFO clubs you could join. Here are three of the best.

Australia
Center for UFO Studies,
Australian Co-Ordination Section (ACOS), PO Box 546,
Gosford, NSW 2250

United Kingdom
Bufora,
15 Freshwater Court,
Crawford Street,
London W1H 1HS

USA
International UFO Registry,
PO Box 1004,
Hammond, Indiana, 46325

Most clubs produce their own magazine or newsletter. There are also several independent magazines available. These are two of the better-known ones.

Flying Saucer Review
FSR Publications Ltd,
West Malling, Maidstone, Kent , England

Australian Flying Saucer Review
PO Box 43, Moorabbin,
Victoria 3181

Try writing to these groups (enclosing a stamped addressed envelope) for information on UFOlogy.

The British UFO Documentation Centre
c/o Alan Fossey, 10 Park Court,
Park Hall Road, London SE21

Center for UFO Studies
c/o Dr J Allen Hynek, 924 Chicago Avenue, Evanston, Illinois 60202, USA

Index